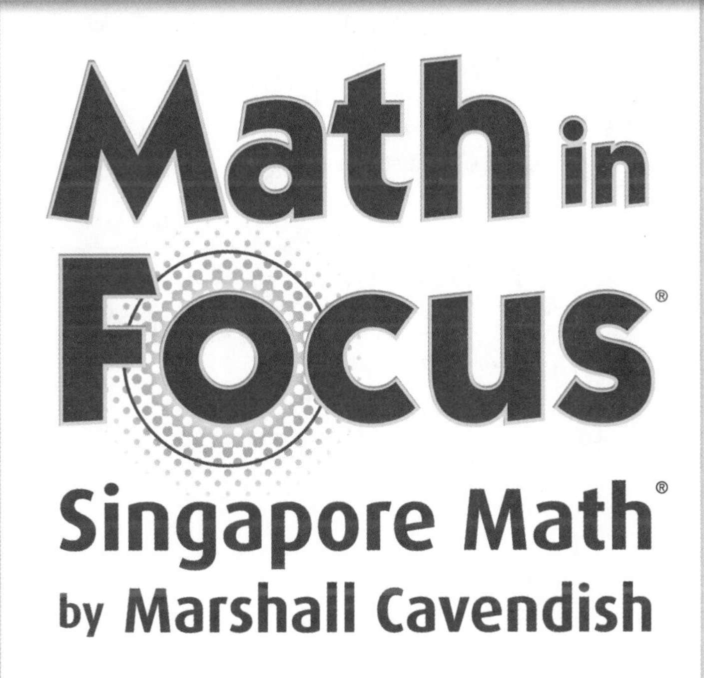




# Extra Practice

**Author**
Meena Newaskar

U.S. Distributor

**Published by Marshall Cavendish Education**
*An imprint of Marshall Cavendish Education Private Limited*
Times Centre, 1 New Industrial Road, Singapore 536196
Customer Service Hotline: (65) 6213 9444
U.S. Office Tel: (1-914) 332 8888 Fax: (1-914) 332 8882
E-mail: tmesales@mceducation.com
Website: www.mceducation.com

Distributed by
**Houghton Mifflin Harcourt**
222 Berkeley Street
Boston, MA 02116
Tel: 617-351-5000
Website: www.hmheducation.com/mathinfocus

First published 2015



*Math in Focus*® Extra Practice 2B
ISBN 978-0-544-19403-8

Printed in Singapore

1 2 3 4 5 6 7 8 1401 20 19 18 17 16 15
4500463691 A B C D E

# Contents

## Chapter 13 Customary Measurement of Length



## Chapter 14 Time



## Chapter 15 Multiplication Tables of 3 and 4

## Introducing

# Math in Focus®

### Extra Practice

*Extra Practice 2A* and *2B*, written to complement *Math in Focus®: Singapore Math® by Marshall Cavendish* Grade 2, offer further practice very similar to the Practice exercises in the Student Books and Workbooks for on-level students.

*Extra Practice* provides ample questions to reinforce all the concepts taught, and includes challenging questions in the Put on Your Thinking Cap! pages. These pages provide extra nonroutine problem-solving opportunities, strengthening critical thinking skills.

*Extra Practice* is an excellent option for homework, or may be used in class or after school. It is intended for students who simply need more practice to become confident, or secure students who are aiming for excellence.

Name: ______________________ Date: ______________

# CHAPTER 10 Mental Math and Estimation

## Lesson 1 Meaning of Sum

**Find the sum of the numbers.**

**1.** 512 and 350

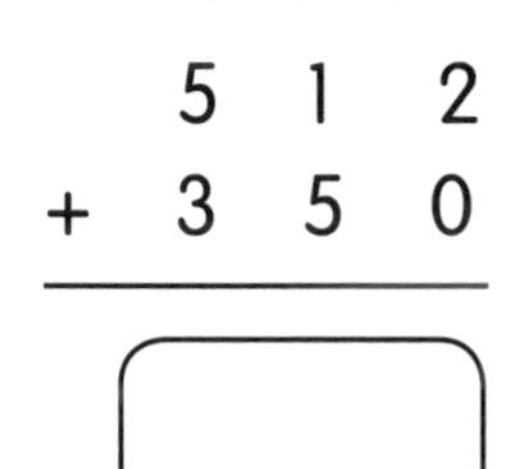

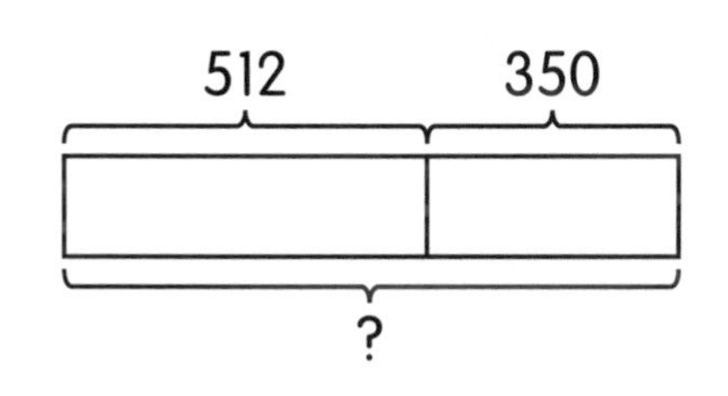


The sum of ________ and ________ is ________.

**2.** 469 and 108

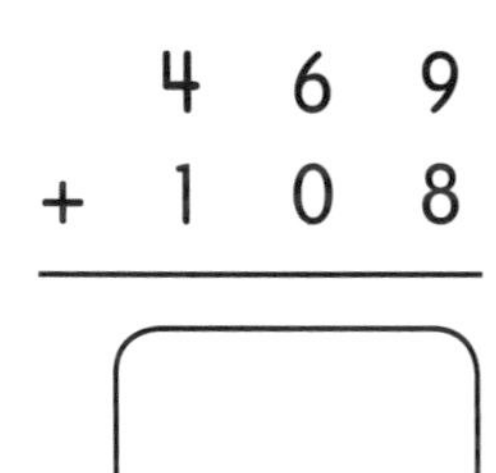

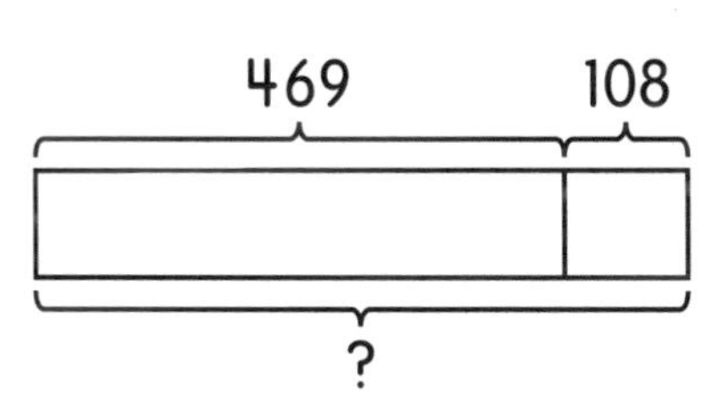


The sum of ________ and ________ is ________.

**3.** 275 and 354

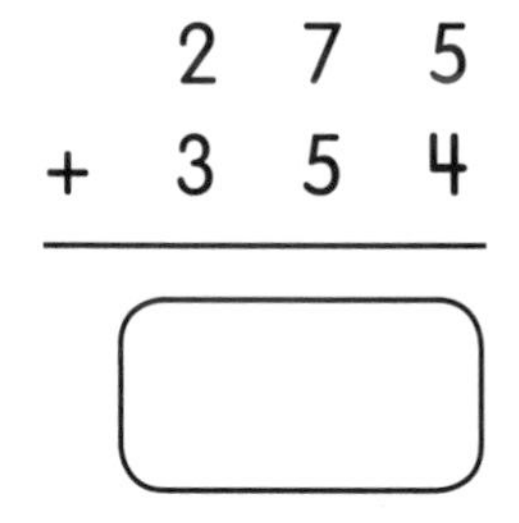

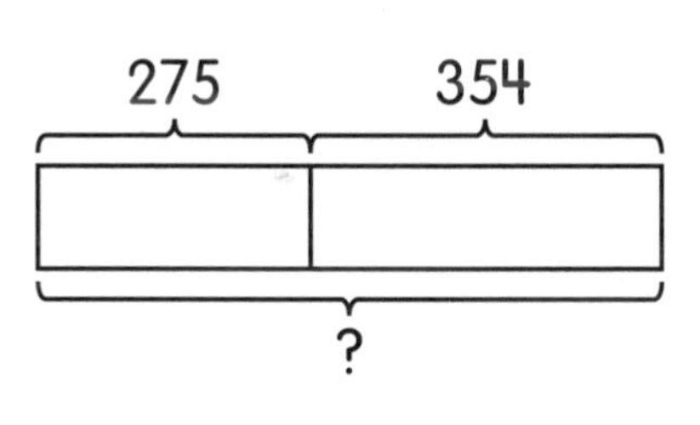


The sum of ________ and ________ is ________.

Name: ______________________ Date: ______________

**Solve.**
**Use bar models to help you.**

**4.** Julia saves $240.
Warrick saves $550.
Find the sum of money they save.

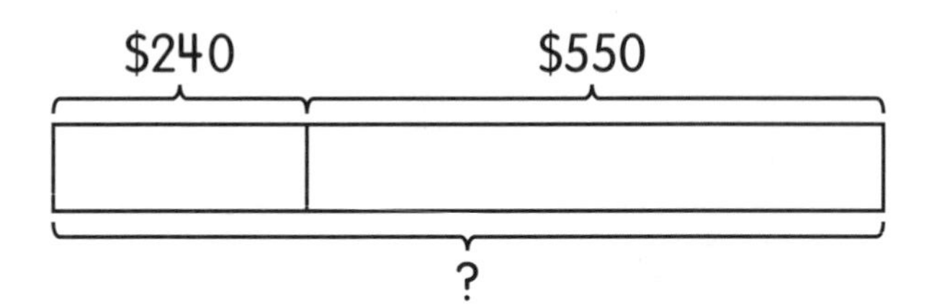


The sum of money they save is $________.

**5.** Alan writes two numbers.
One number is 529.
The other number is 360.
Find the sum of the two numbers.

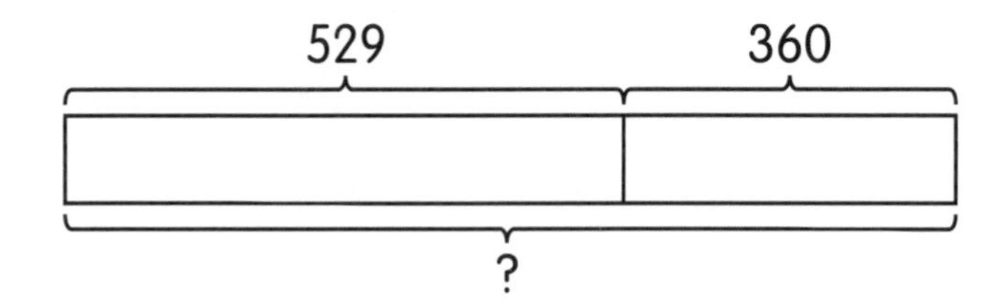


The sum of the two numbers is ________.

Name: ____________________ Date: ____________

# Lesson 2 Mental Addition

**Add mentally.**
**Fill in the blanks.**

**1.** $24 + 3 =$ ______

**2.** $65 + 4 =$ ______

**3.** $87 + 2 =$ ______

**4.** $36 + 3 =$ ______

**5.** $54 + 5 =$ ______

**6.** $71 + 6 =$ ______

**Find the missing numbers.**
**Add mentally.**

**7.** $35 + 6 = ?$

$35 +$ __10__ $=$ __45__

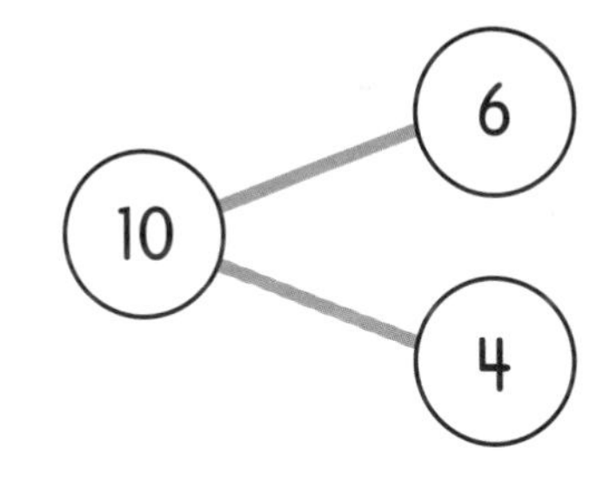


______ − ______ = ______

So, $35 + 6 =$ ______.

**8.** $67 + 5 = ?$

$67 +$ ______ $=$ ______

______ − ______ = ______

So, $67 + 5 =$ ______.

Name: ______________________ Date: ______________

9. 86 + 8 = ________

10. 26 + 9 = ________

11. 49 + 3 = ________

12. 58 + 4 = ________

**Find the missing numbers.**
**Add mentally.**

13. 236 + 2 = ?

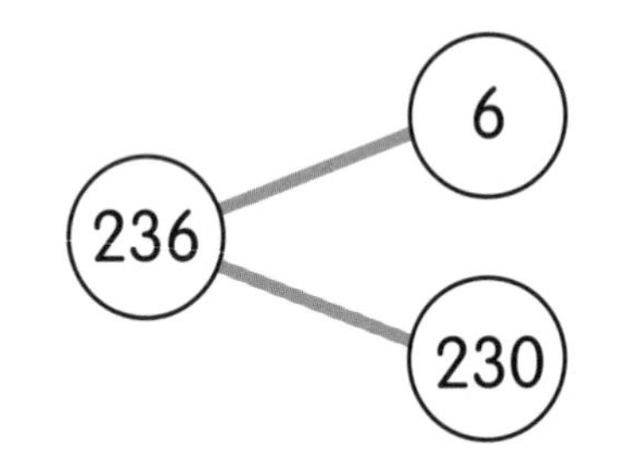


6 + ________ = ________

________ + ________ = ________

So, 236 + 2 = ________.

14. 473 + 2 = ________

15. 765 + 3 = ________

16. 267 + 1 = ________

17. 365 + 4 = ________

18. 549 + 7 = ?

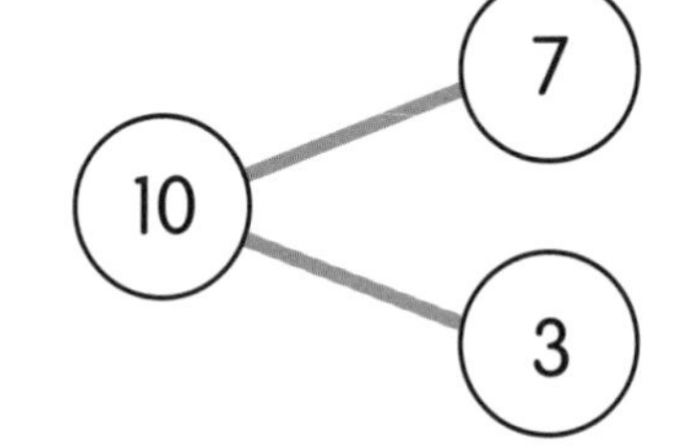


549 + ________ = ________

________ – ________ = ________

So, 549 + 7 = ________.

Name: ____________________ Date: ____________

**19.** 388 + 9 = ______

**20.** 454 + 7 = ______

**21.** 356 + 9 = ______

**22.** 157 + 3 = ______

**Find the missing numbers.**
**Add mentally.**

**23.** 425 + 30 = ?

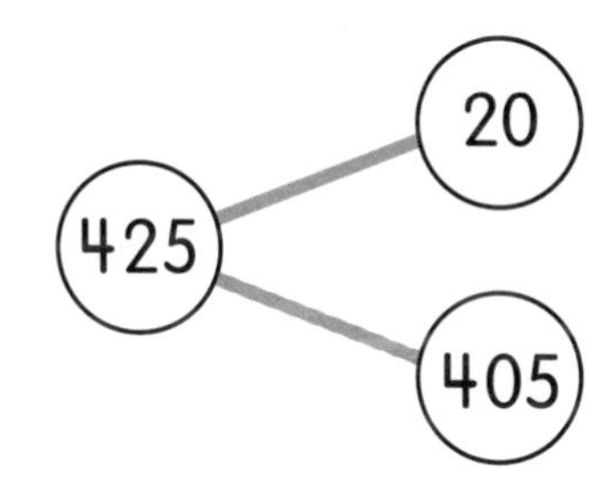


______ + 30 = ______

______ + ______ = ______

So, 425 + 30 = ______.

**24.** 716 + 50 = ______

**25.** 549 + 50 = ______

**26.** 657 + 40 = ______

**27.** 835 + 30 = ______

**Find the missing numbers.**
**Add mentally.**

**28.** 677 + 60 = ?

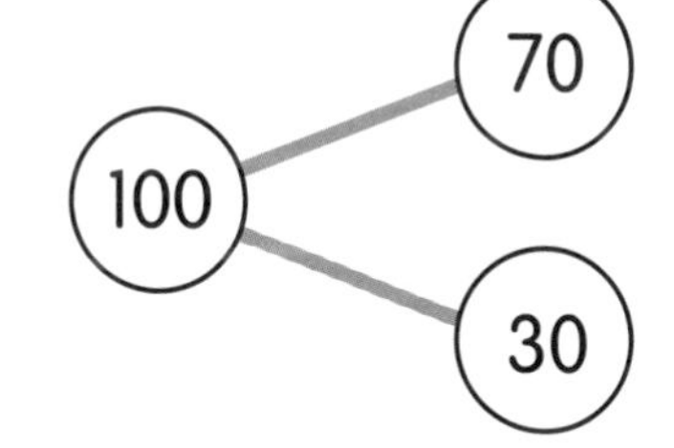


677 + ______ = ______

______ − ______ = ______

So, 677 + 60 = ______.

Name: ______________________ Date: ______________

**29.** 351 + 70 = ________

**30.** 864 + 90 = ________

**31.** 786 + 80 = ________

**32.** 472 + 60 = ________

**Fill in the missing numbers.**
**Add mentally.**

**33.** 267 + 200 = ?

________ + 200 = ________

________ + 67 = ________

267
200
67

So, 267 + 200 = ________.

**34.** 351 + 200 = ________

**35.** 864 + 100 = ________

**36.** 408 + 500 = ________

**37.** 682 + 200 = ________

Name: ______________________ Date: ______________

# Lesson 3 Meaning of Difference

**Find the difference between the numbers.**

**1.** 82 – 37

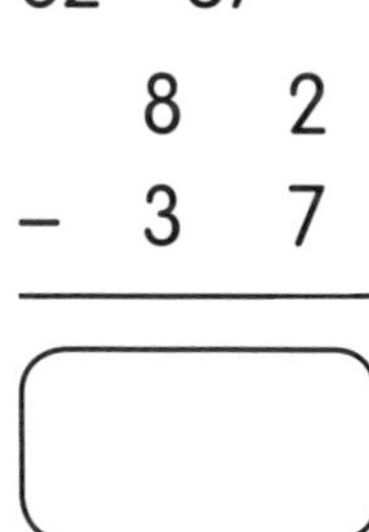


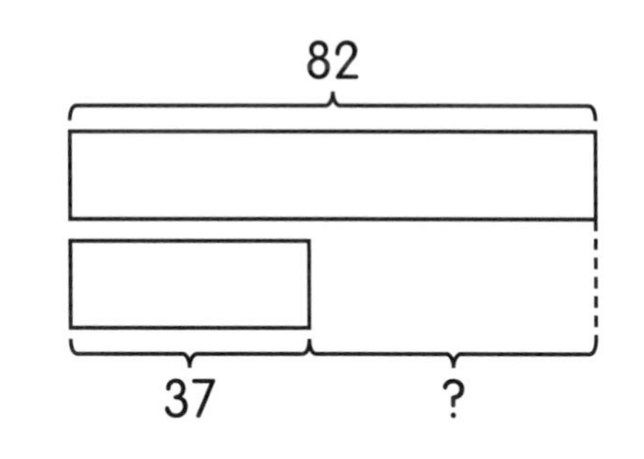


The difference between 82 and 37 is ________.

**2.** 650 – 420

$$\begin{array}{r} 6\ 5\ 0 \\ -\ 4\ 2\ 0 \\ \hline \end{array}$$

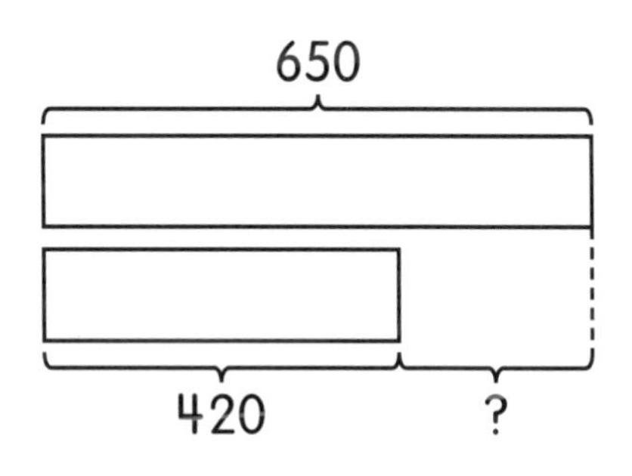


The difference between 650 and 420 is ________.

**3.** 900 – 575

$$\begin{array}{r} 9\ 0\ 0 \\ -\ 5\ 7\ 5 \\ \hline \end{array}$$

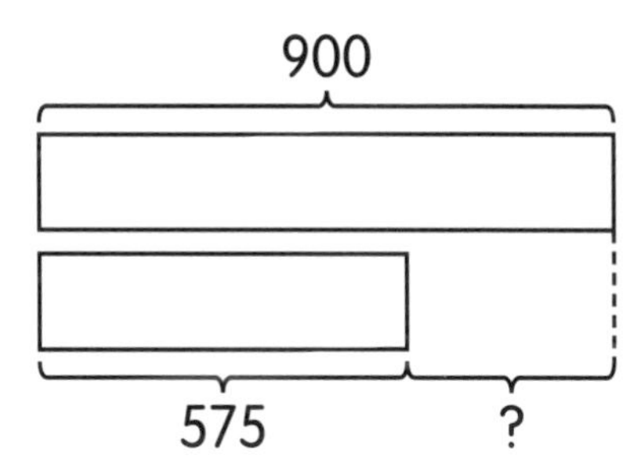


The difference between 900 and 575 is ________.

Name: ______________________ Date: ______________

**Solve.**
**Use bar models to help you.**

**4.** Sally sold 450 burgers.
Jenny sold 230 burgers.
Find the difference between the number of burgers they sold.

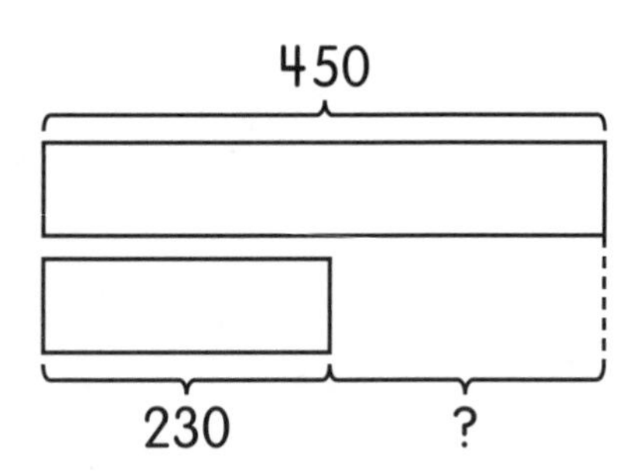


The difference is ________ burgers.

**5.** Kaylene baked 150 muffins on Tuesday.
She baked 77 muffins on Thursday.
What is the difference between these two amounts?

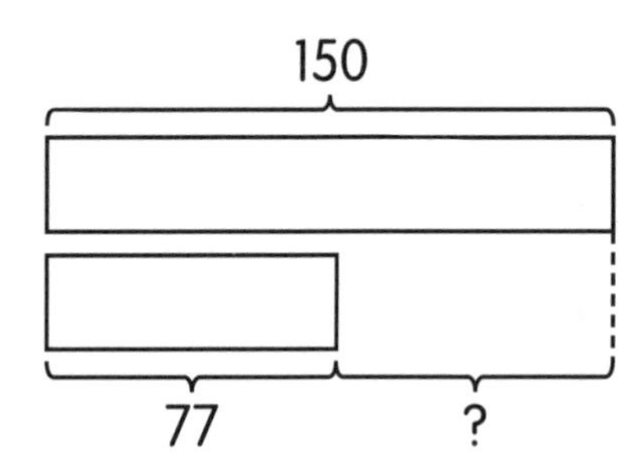


The difference is ________muffins.

Name: ______________________ Date: ______________

# Lesson 4 Mental Subtraction

**Subtract mentally.**
**Fill in the blanks.**

**1.** 29 – 2 = ______

**2.** 47 – 1 = ______

**3.** 65 – 4 = ______

**4.** 54 – 4 = ______

**5.** 79 – 7 = ______

**6.** 88 – 6 = ______

**Find the missing numbers.**
**Subtract mentally.**

**7.** 53 – 9 = ?

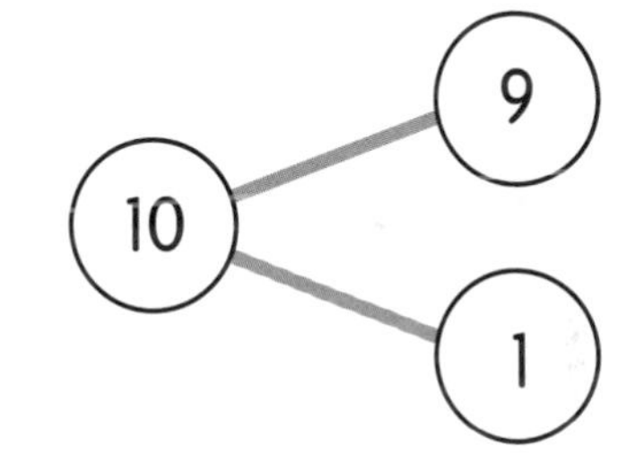


53 – 10 = 43

______ + ______ = ______

So, 53 – 9 = ______.

**8.** 74 – 6 = ?

______ – 10 = ______

______ + ______ = ______

So, 74 – 6 = ______.

Name: ______________________ Date: ______________

**9.** 61 – 7 = ________ **10.** 32 – 9 = ________

**11.** 42 – 8 = ________ **12.** 94 – 5 = ________

**Find the missing numbers.**
**Subtract mentally.**

**13.** 536 – 5 = ?

__6__ – 5 = __1__

________ + ________ = ________

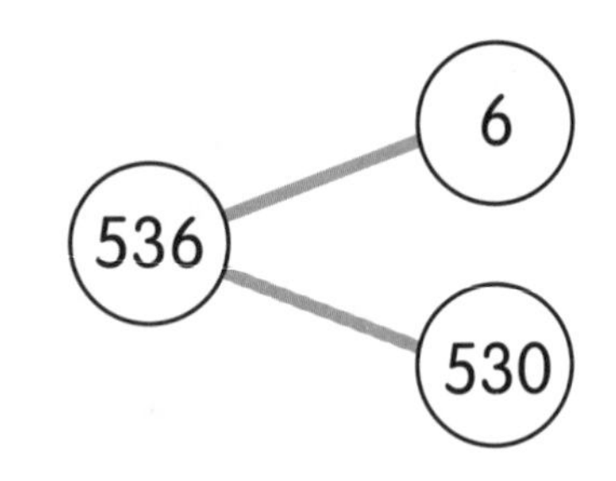


So, 536 – 5 = ________.

**14.** 688 – 4 = ________ **15.** 829 – 7 = ________

**16.** 529 – 1 = ________ **17.** 486 – 4 = ________

**18.** 473 – 5 = ?

473 – ________ = ________

________ + ________ = ________

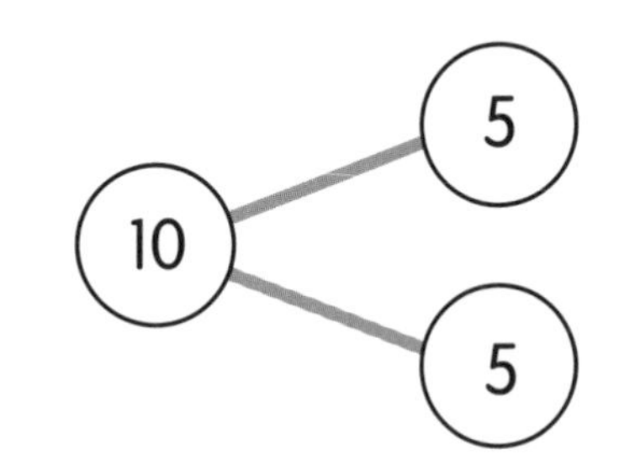


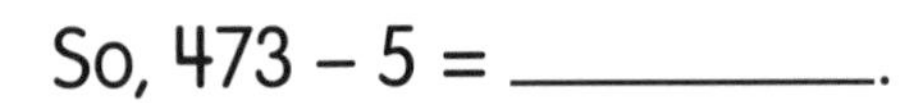
So, 473 – 5 = ________.

Name: ______________________ Date: ______________

**19.** 764 – 8 = ________

**20.** 821 – 9 = ________

**21.** 423 – 5 = ________

**22.** 651 – 7 = ________

**Find the missing numbers.**
**Subtract mentally.**

**23.** 492 – 30 = ?

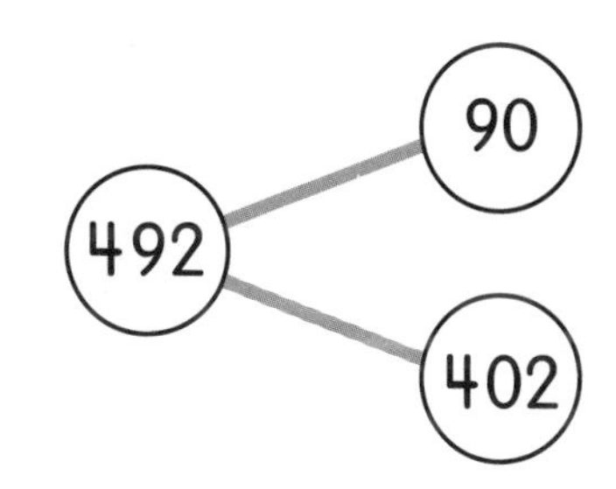


________ – 30 = ________

________ + ________ = ________

So, 492 – 30 = ________.

**24.** 286 – 60 = ________

**25.** 763 – 50 = ________

**26.** 258 – 10 = ________

**27.** 657 – 40 = ________

**Find the missing numbers.**
**Add mentally.**

**28.** 361 – 70 = ?

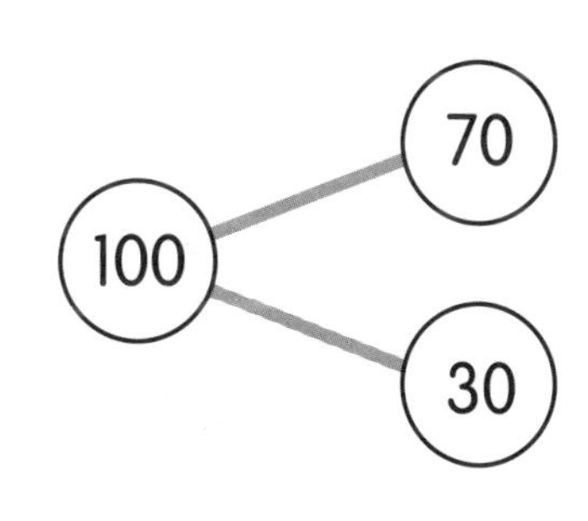


________ – 100 = ________

________ + ________ = ________

So, 361 – 70 = ________.

Name: ______________________ Date: ______________

**29.** 530 – 90 = ________

**30.** 240 – 50 = ________

**31.** 560 – 80 = ________

**32.** 820 – 90 = ________

**Find the missing numbers.**
**Subtract mentally.**

**33.** 428 – 200 = ?

________ – 200 = ________

________ + ________ = ________

So, 428 – 200 = ________.

428: 28, 400

**34.** 645 – 300 = ________

**35.** 831 – 600 = ________

**36.** 780 – 400 = ________

**37.** 905 – 700 = ________

Name: ______________________ Date: ______________

# Lesson 5 Rounding Numbers to Estimate

**Mark each number with an X on the number line.**
**Round each number to the nearest ten.**
**Circle it on the number line.**
**Then fill in the blanks.**

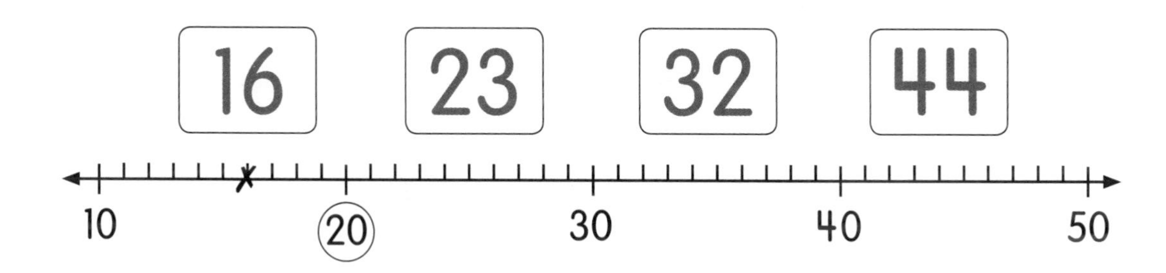


**1.** 16 is nearer to ___20___ than to ___10___.

16 is about ________ when rounded to the nearest ten.

**2.** 23 is nearer to ________ than to ________.

23 is about ________ when rounded to the nearest ten.

**3.** 32 is nearer to ________ than to ________.

32 is about ________ when rounded to the nearest ten.

**4.** 44 is nearer to ________ than to ________.

44 is about ________ when rounded to the nearest ten.

Name: ______________________________ Date: ________________

**Look at the digits in the tens place.
Then fill in the blanks.**

**5.** 78 78 is between ________ and ________.

**6.** 91 91 is between ________ and ________.

**7.** 458 458 is between ________ and ________.

**8.** 853 853 is between ________ and ________.

**Mark each number with an *X* on the number line.
Round each number to the nearest ten.
Circle the number on the number line.
Then fill in the last column of the table.**

| | Number | Number line | Write using 'is about' |
|---|---|---|---|
| **9.** | 425 | 420 — 430 | ______ is about ______. |
| **10.** | 652 | 650 — 660 | ______ is about ______. |
| **11.** | 856 | 850 — 860 | ______ is about ______. |

Name: ______________________ Date: ______________

**Complete the table.**

| | Number | Rounded to the nearest ten | Write using 'is about' |
|---|---|---|---|
| **12.** | 98 | | ______ is about ______. |
| **13.** | 125 | | ______ is about ______. |
| **14.** | 369 | | ______ is about ______. |
| **15.** | 424 | | ______ is about ______. |
| **16.** | 652 | | ______ is about ______. |
| **17.** | 856 | | ______ is about ______. |

**The numbers in each problem are rounded to the nearest ten.**
**Find the greatest and least number that was rounded.**
**Use the number line to help you.**

**18.** A camera costs about $50.

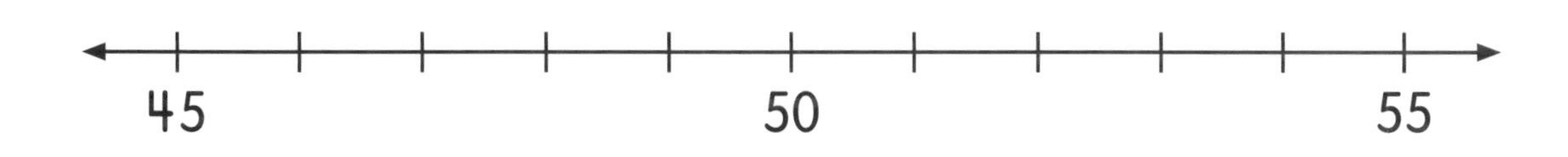


The greatest amount the camera could cost is $______.

The least amount the camera could cost is $______.

Name: ______________________ Date: ______________

**19.** A swimming pool is about 80 meters long.

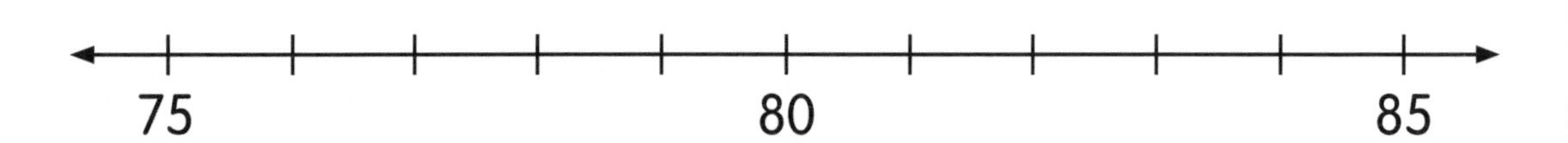


The greatest length the pool could be is ________ meters.

The least length the pool could be is ________ meters.

**20.** The mass of a bag of rice is about 500 grams.

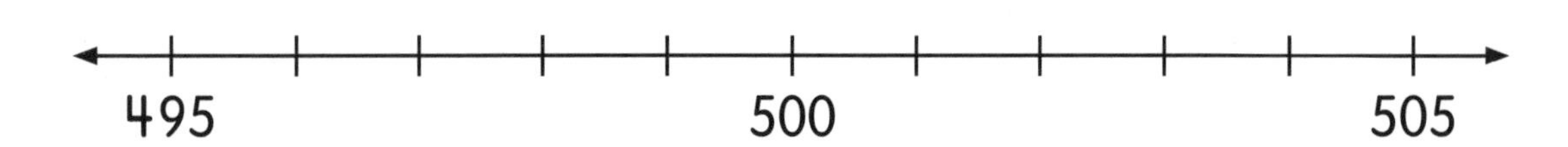


The greatest mass the rice could be ________ grams.

The least mass the rice could be ________ grams.

Name: ______________________ Date: ______________

**Find the sum or difference.**
**Then round each number to the nearest ten.**
**Estimate the sum or difference to check that the answer is reasonable.**

**21.** 268 + 323 = __________

268 is about __________.

323 is about __________.

__________ + __________ = __________

So, 268 + 323 is about __________.

Is the answer reasonable? Explain.

______________________________________________

**22.** 479 – 124 = __________

479 is about __________.

124 is about __________.

__________ – __________ = __________

So, 479 – 124 is about __________.

Is the answer reasonable? Explain.

______________________________________________

Name: ______________________ Date: ______________

**Find the sum or difference.**
**Then round each number to the nearest ten.**
**Estimate the sum or difference to check that the answer is reasonable.**

**23.** 235 + 552 = ________

Check: ________ + ________ = ________

Is the answer reasonable? Explain.

______________________________________________

**24.** 574 – 296 = ________

Check: ________ – ________ = ________

Is the answer reasonable? Explain.

______________________________________________

Name: ______________________________ Date: ____________________

**Fill in the missing numbers or words.**

**25.** Daniel has $100 to buy these items.
Round the cost of each item to the nearest ten.
Then estimate the total cost.

A school bag costs $38.

**a.** $38 is __________ when rounded to the nearest ten.

A box of crayons costs $11.

**b.** $11 is __________ when rounded to the nearest ten.

A pair of shoes costs $27.

**c.** $27 is __________ when rounded to the nearest ten.

A textbook costs $18.

**d.** $18 is __________ when rounded to the nearest ten.

The estimated total cost is $__________.

Does Daniel have enough money to pay for all the items?

__________.

Name: ______________________ Date: ______________

1. Juliana thinks of two numbers.
   The sum of the two numbers is 20.
   The difference between the two numbers is 6.
   What are the numbers?

   The numbers are ________ and ________.

2. Study the numbers in A.
   Use the pattern in A to find the missing numbers in B.

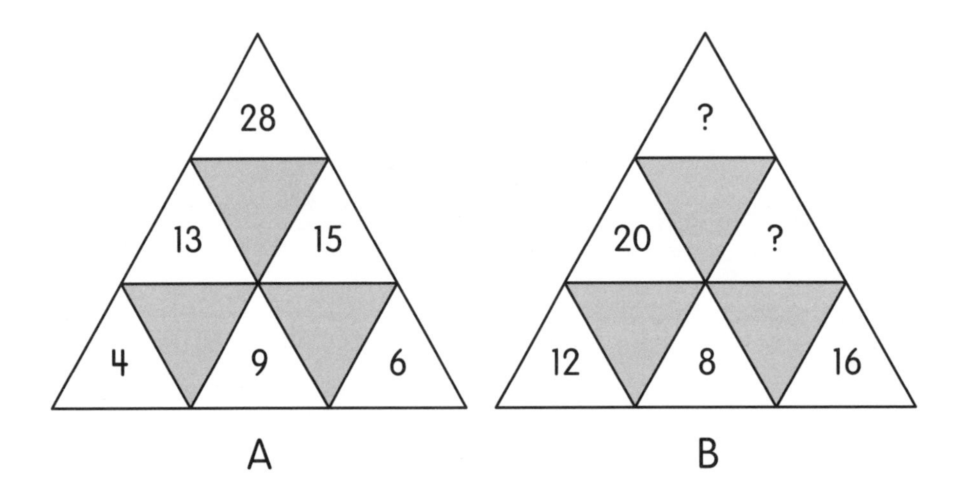


The missing numbers are ________ and ________.

Name: ______________________ Date: ______________

# Lesson 1 Coins and Bills

**Circle the bills that make the given amount.**

**1.**

$5 =

**2.**

$10 =

**3.**

$20 =

Name: ______________________ Date: ______________

## Circle the coins that make one dollar.

**4.**

 =

**5.**

 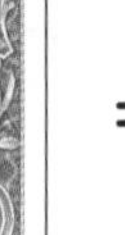 =

## Find the value of the coins.
## Then write *less than, equal to,* or *more than.*

**6.**

______________________ \$1.

**7.**

______________________ \$1.

Name: ______________________ Date: ______________

**8.**

______________ $1.

## Write the amount of money.

**9.**

$________

**10.**

$________

Name: ______________________ Date: ______________

**Write the amount of money.**

**11.** forty-five cents $______

**12.** thirty-seven dollars $______

**13.** ninety-eight dollars and three cents $______

**Fill in the blanks.**

**14.** $0.06 ______ dollars ______ cents

**15.** $2.33 ______ dollars ______ cents

**16.** $10.28 ______ dollars ______ cents

**17.** $24.74 ______ dollars ______ cents

**18.** $40.52 ______ dollars ______ cents

Name: ______________________________ Date: ____________________

## Complete.

**19.**

Ben has __________ dollars

and __________ cents or

$__________.

**20.**

Sheena has __________ dollars

and __________ cents or

$__________.

Name: ______________________ Date: ______________

## Write the amount of money in two ways.

**21.**

_______¢ or $_______

**22.**

_______¢ or $_______

**23.**

_______¢ or $_______

Name: ______________________ Date: ______________

**24.**

_______¢ or $_______

**25.**

_______¢ or $_______

Name: ____________________ Date: ____________

**Write the amount in dollars and cents.**

**26.** 236¢ ____________

**27.** 327¢ ____________

**28.** 28¢ ____________

**29.** 680¢ ____________

**30.** 115¢ ____________

**31.** 425¢ ____________

**Write the amount in cents.**

**32.** $1.63 ____________

**33.** $4 ____________

**34.** $3.48 ____________

**35.** $5.60 ____________

**36.** $0.70 ____________

**37.** $9.16 ____________

Name: ______________________________ Date: ____________________

# Lesson 2 Comparing Amounts of Money

**Compare the amounts.**
**Complete the tables and fill in the blanks.**

**1.** Shania
$12.30

| Dollars | Cents |
| --- | --- |
| | |

David
$17.50

| Dollars | Cents |
| --- | --- |
| | |

$________ is more than $________.

$________ is less than $________.

**2.** Pete
$45.62

| Dollars | Cents |
| --- | --- |
| | |

Roslyn
$45.40

| Dollars | Cents |
| --- | --- |
| | |

$________ is more than $________.

$________ is less than $________.

Name: ______________________ Date: ______________

**3.**

$25.45

| Dollars | Cents |
|---|---|
| | |

$25.60

| Dollars | Cents |
|---|---|
| | |

$26.50

| Dollars | Cents |
|---|---|
| | |

Are all of these amounts the same? __________

$________ is the greatest amount.

$________ is the least amount.

**4.**

$44.70

| Dollars | Cents |
|---|---|
| | |

$43.70

| Dollars | Cents |
|---|---|
| | |

$44.75

| Dollars | Cents |
|---|---|
| | |

Are all of these amounts the same? __________

$________ is the greatest amount.

$________ is the least amount.

Name: ______________________ Date: ______________

**Write the amount in each set.**
**Then check (✓) the set that has the greater value.**

**5.**

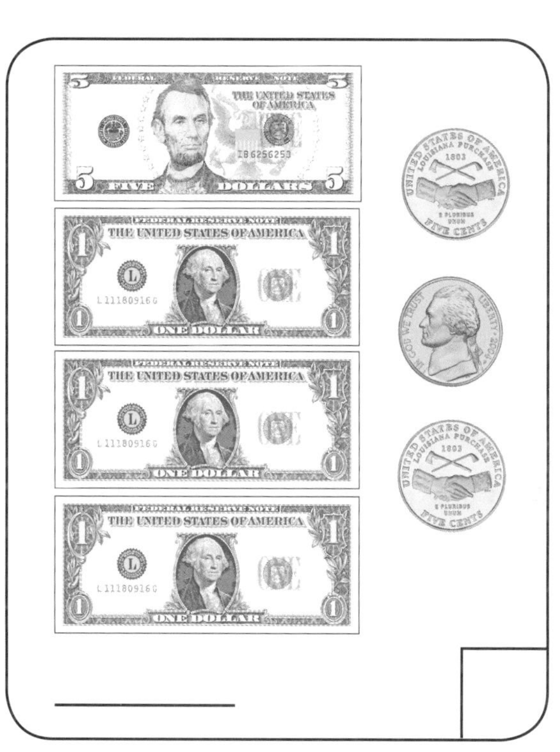

**6.**

Name: ______________________ Date: ______________

**Circle the amount that is less.**

**7.** $7.25 $3.60

**8.** $13.45 $13.54

**9.** $33.98 $86.98

**Circle the amount that is greater.**

**10.** $65.80 $6.80

**11.** $5.70 $7.50

**12.** $70.70 $7.50

**Compare the amounts.**

**$2.80 $28.00 $2.08**

**13.** Which amount is the least? ________

**14.** Which amount is the greatest? ________

**15.** Order the amounts from least to greatest.

________, ________, ________

least greatest

Name: ____________________ Date: ____________

# Lesson 3 Real-World Problems: Money

**Solve.**

**Draw bar models to help you.**

**1.** Gary buys a ruler for 13¢ and an eraser for 10¢.
He gives the cashier $1.
How much change does he get?

He gets ________ in change.

**2.** Mrs. Jimenez has $100.
She spends $40 on clothes, and $15 on food.
How much money does Mrs. Jimenez have left?

Mrs. Jimenez has $________ left.

Name: ______________________ Date: ______________

**3.** Marcel buys a pair of shoes for $20.
His sister buys a pair of shoes that costs $5 more.
How much do they pay in all?

They pay $________ in all.

**4.** A model boat costs $45.50.
A model car costs $10.25 less.
A model train set costs $68.
How much more does the model train set cost than the model car?

The model train set costs $________ more than the model car.

Name: ______________________ Date: ______________

**Solve.**
**Draw bar models to help you.**

**5.** Twyla goes to the supermarket.
She has $60.50 in her purse.
She buys some fish for $12.80 and beef for $19.80.
How much money does Twyla have left?

Twyla has $________ left.

**6.** Carmen buys a watch and a storybook.
She has $17.70 left.
How much money did Carmen have at first?

Carmen had $________ at first.

Name: ______________________ Date: ______________

**7.** A pair of shoes costs $29.50.
A bag costs $7.80 less.
How much does Rain pay for these two items?

Rain pays $________ for these two items.

**8.** David saves $15.70. Grace saves $5.80 more.
They use all their money to buy a birthday present for their mother.
How much does the present cost?

The present costs $________.

Name: ______________________ Date: ______________

1. Mr. and Mrs. Brown went to a museum with their 9-year-old son, 6-year-old daughter, and 2-year-old daughter.
How much did the family spend on the tickets in all?

**Entrance Fees**

Adult: $8
Child (under 12): $4
Child (under 3): free

The family spent $________ on the tickets in all.

Name: ______________________ Date: ______________

**2.** Mrs. Ferrera has five $10 bills.
Which two items did she buy if she spent the greatest amount possible?

handbag

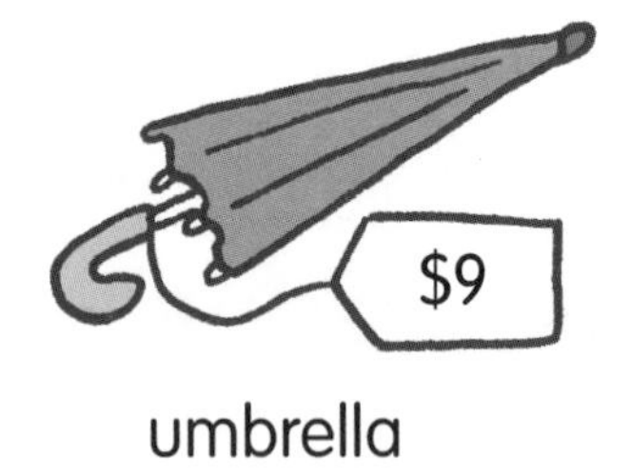


umbrella

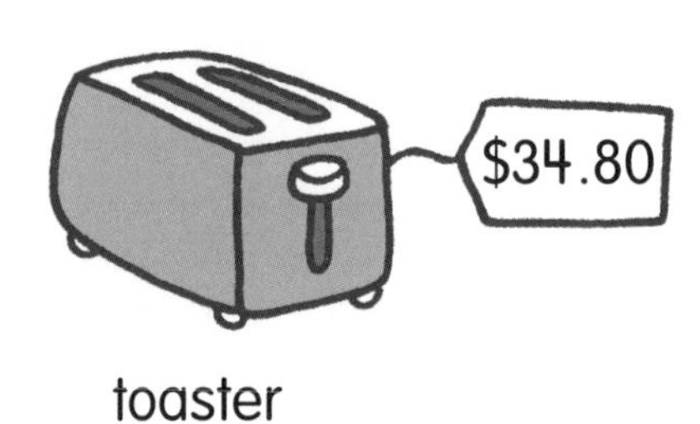


toaster

compact disc

She bought the ______________ and ______________.

Name: ______________________ Date: ______________

# Chapter 12 Fractions

## Lesson 1 Understanding Fractions

**Make a ✔ in the box if the shape is divided into equal parts.**

1.

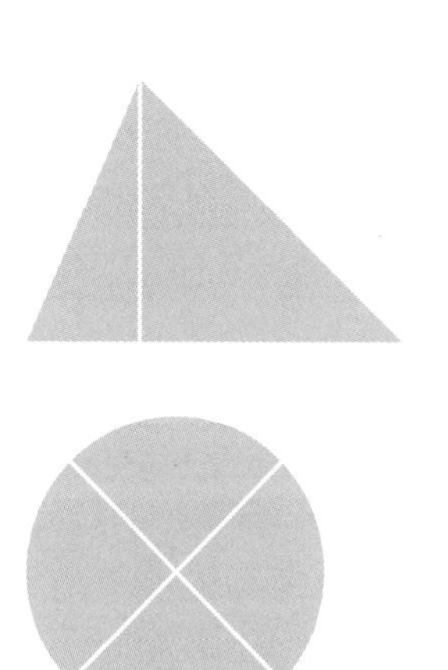

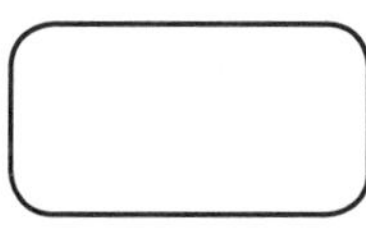

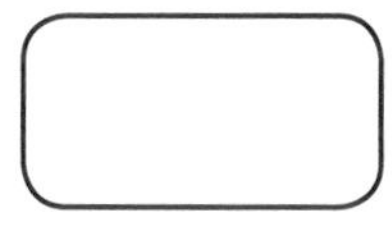

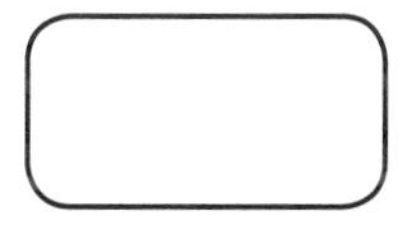

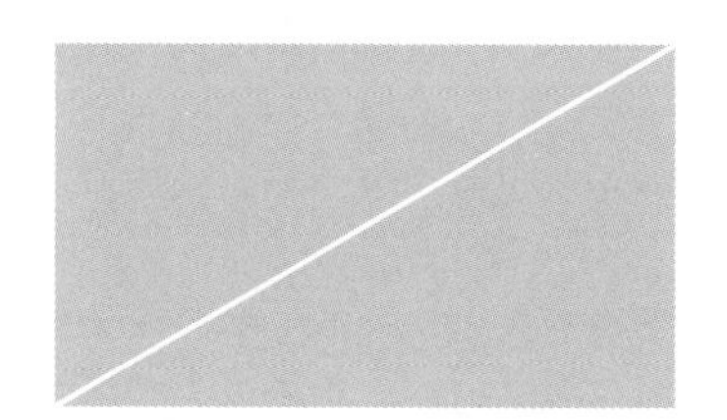

Name: ______________________ Date: ______________

## Circle the fractions that match the picture.

**2.**

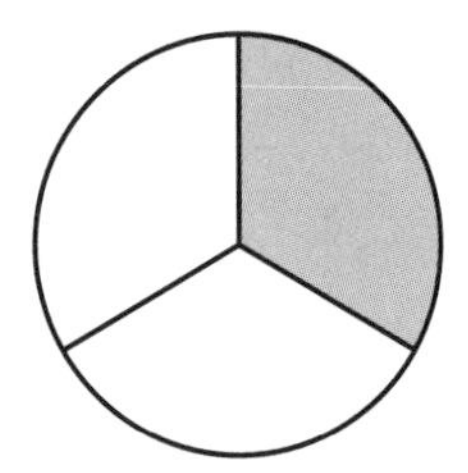

| one-half | $\frac{1}{3}$ | one-third | $\frac{1}{4}$ |
|---|---|---|---|

**3.**

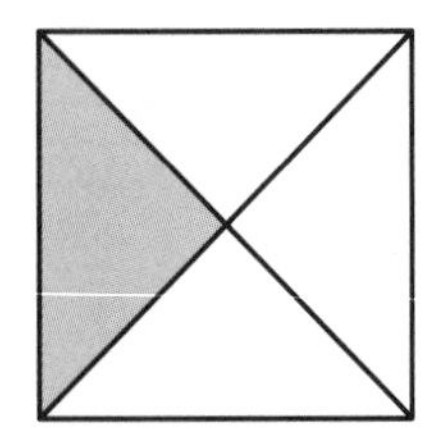

| one-third | 1 | one-quarter | $\frac{1}{2}$ |
|---|---|---|---|

**4.**

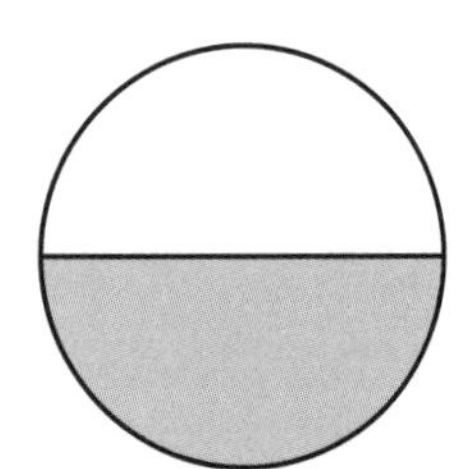

| one-half | $\frac{1}{4}$ | one-third | 1 |
|---|---|---|---|

Name: ______________________ Date: ______________

**Fill in the blanks.**

**5.**

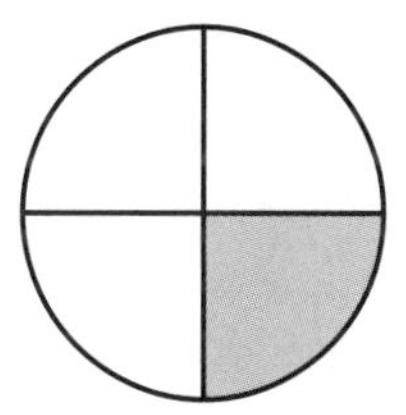

_______ out of _______ equal parts is shaded.

_______ of the figure is shaded.

**6.**

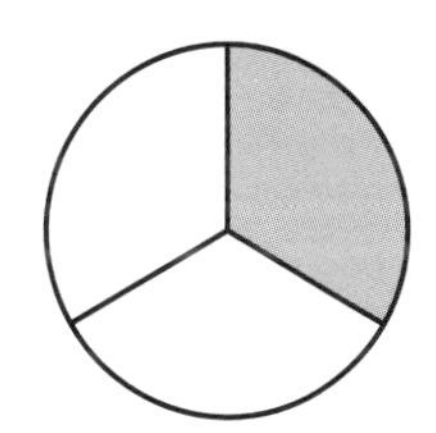

_______ out of _______ equal parts is shaded.

_______ of the figure is shaded.

Name: ______________________ Date: ______________

## Write a fraction for each shaded part.

**7.**

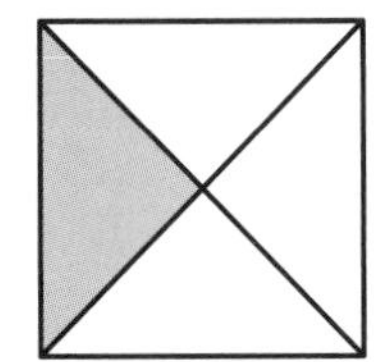

______________

**8.**

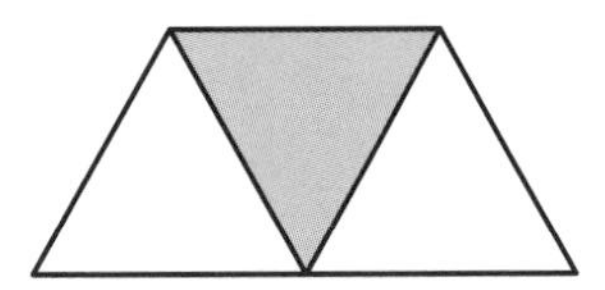

______________

**9.**

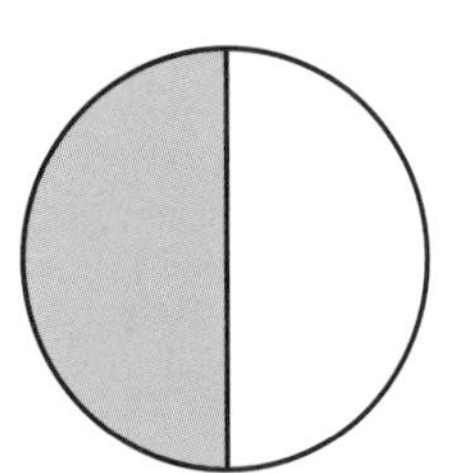

______________

## Shade part(s) of each figure to show the fraction.

**10.** $\frac{1}{4}$

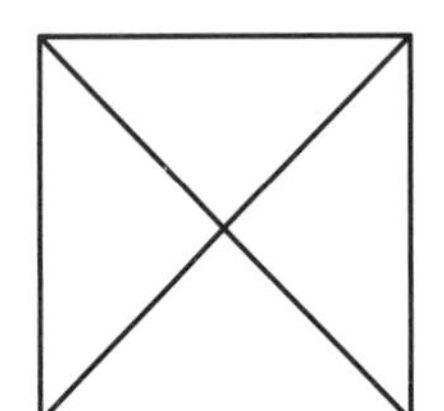

**11.** $\frac{1}{3}$

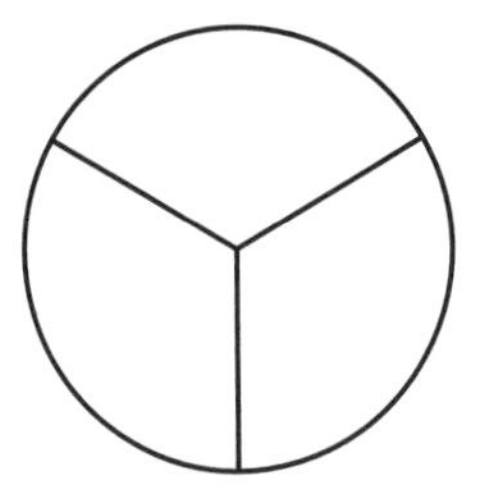

**12.** $\frac{1}{2}$

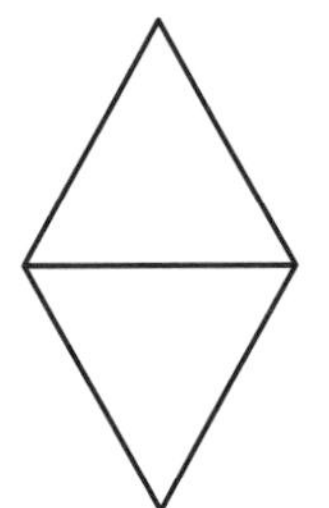

Name: ______________________ Date: ______________

# Lesson 2 Comparing Fractions

**Write the fraction of the shaded part or parts. Then compare the fractions.**

1. 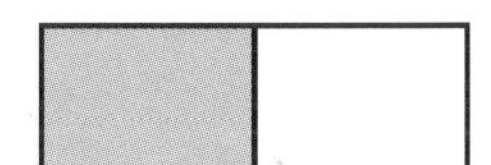

______ is shaded. ______ is shaded.

______ is greater than ______.

______ is less than ______.

2. 

______ is shaded. ______ is shaded.

______ is greater than ______.

______ is less than ______.

3. 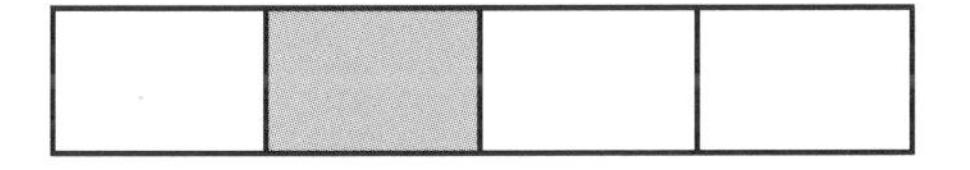

______ is shaded. ______ is shaded.

______ is greater than ______.

______ is less than ______.

Name: ____________________ Date: ____________

**Compare.**
**Fill in the blanks with > or <.**

**4.**

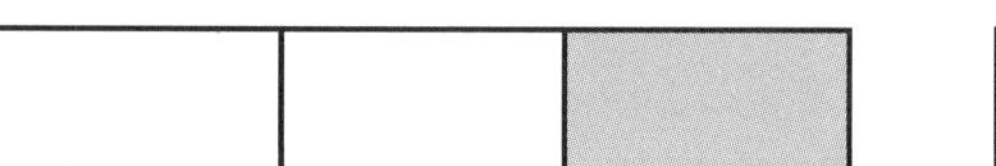

$\frac{1}{3}$ is shaded.

$\frac{1}{2}$ is shaded.

$\frac{1}{2}$ ______ $\frac{1}{3}$

$\frac{1}{3}$ ______ $\frac{1}{2}$

**5.**

$\frac{1}{4}$ is shaded.

$\frac{1}{2}$ is shaded.

$\frac{1}{4}$ ______ $\frac{1}{2}$

$\frac{1}{2}$ ______ $\frac{1}{4}$

**Order the fractions from greatest to least.**

**6.**

______, ______, ______
greatest least

Name: ______________________ Date: ______________

# Lesson 3 Adding and Subtracting Like Fractions

**Write the fraction for the shaded parts.**

1.

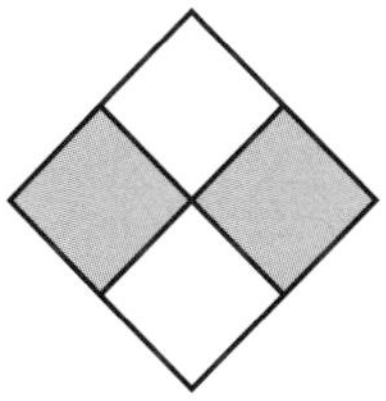

______

2.

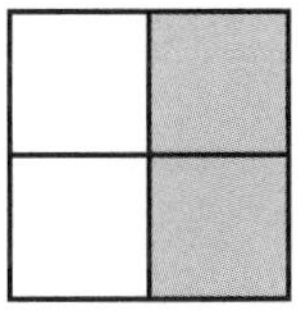

______

3.

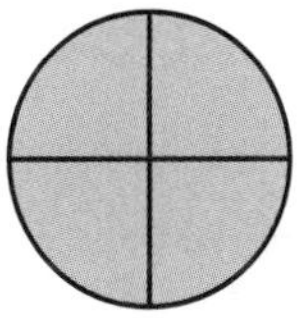

______

**Add.**
**Shade the parts to show the sum.**

4.

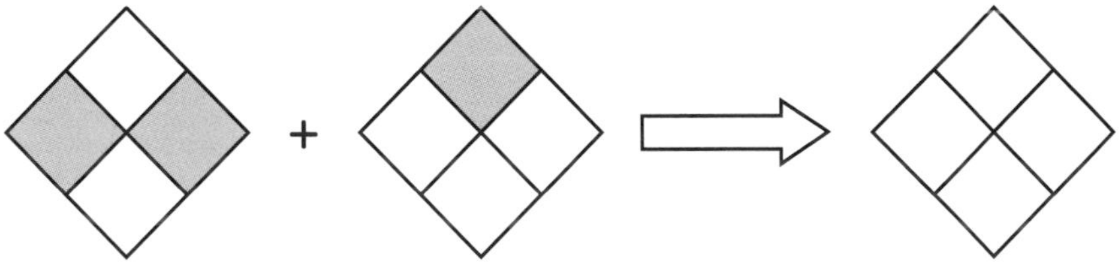

5.

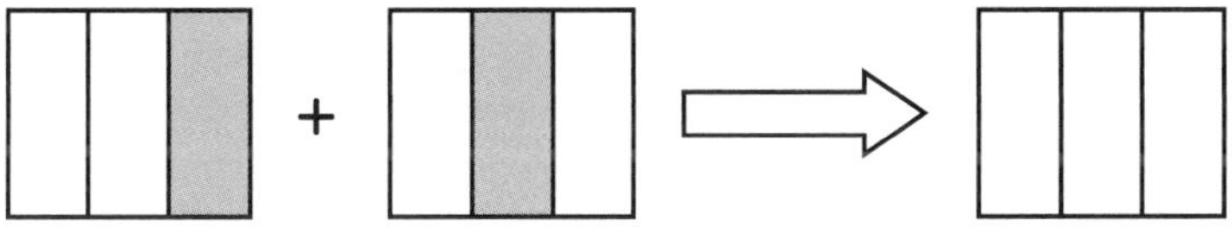

6.

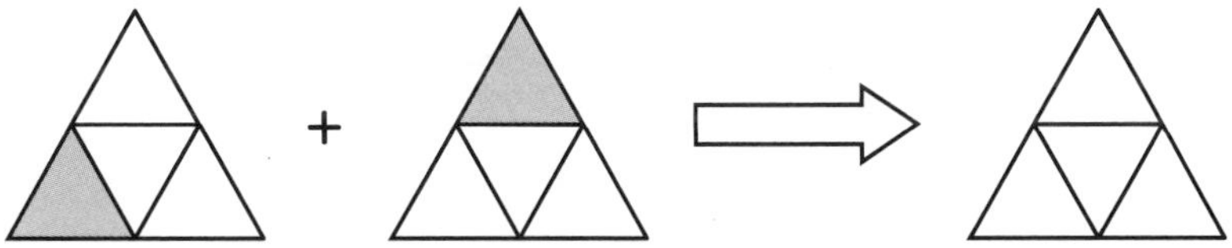

Name: ________________________ Date: ____________

**Add.**

**Use models to help you.**

**7.** $\frac{1}{4} + \frac{2}{4} =$ ________

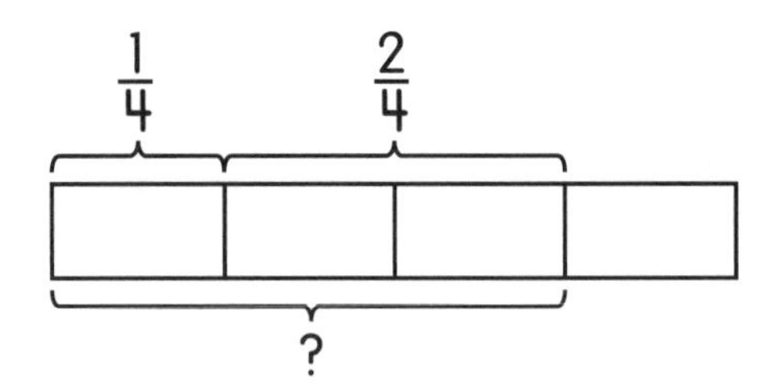


**8.** $\frac{1}{3} + \frac{1}{3} =$ ________

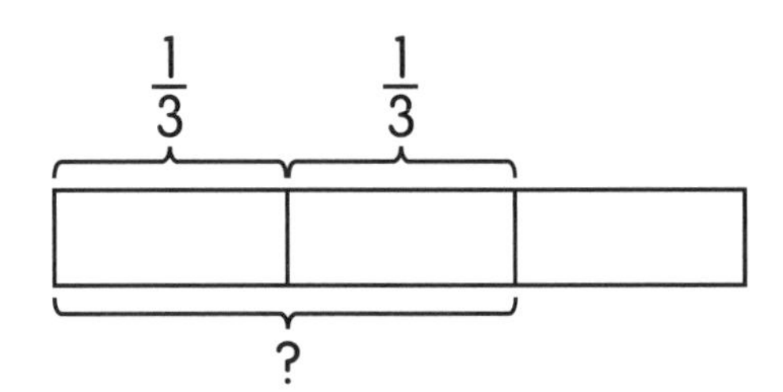


**9.** $\frac{1}{2} + \frac{1}{2} =$ ________

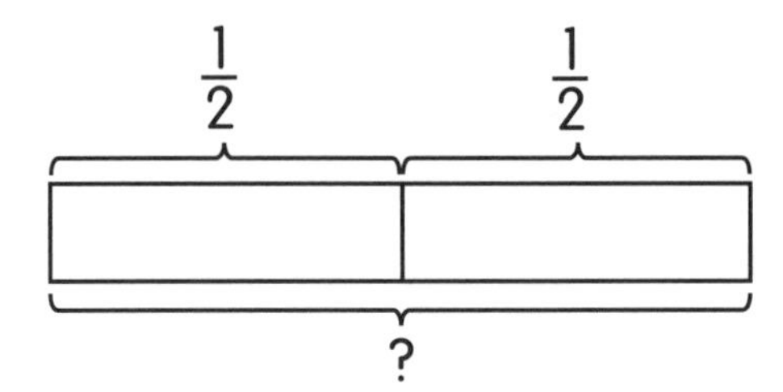

Name: ______________________ Date: ______________

**Subtract.**
**Shade the parts to show the difference.**

**10.**

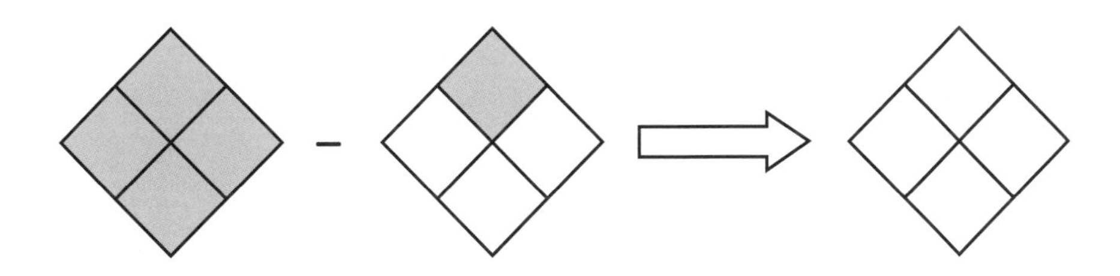

**11.**

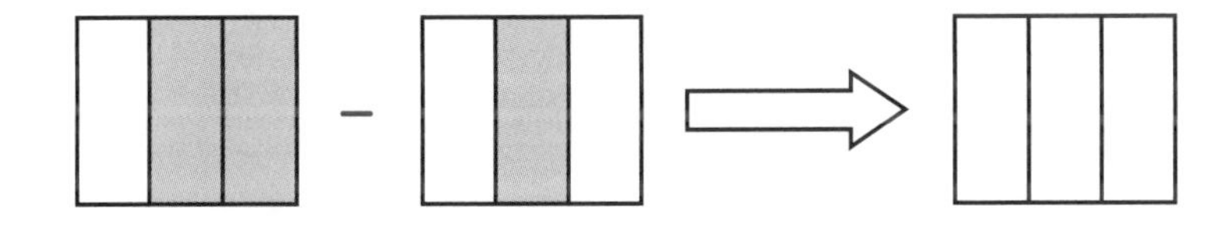

**12.**

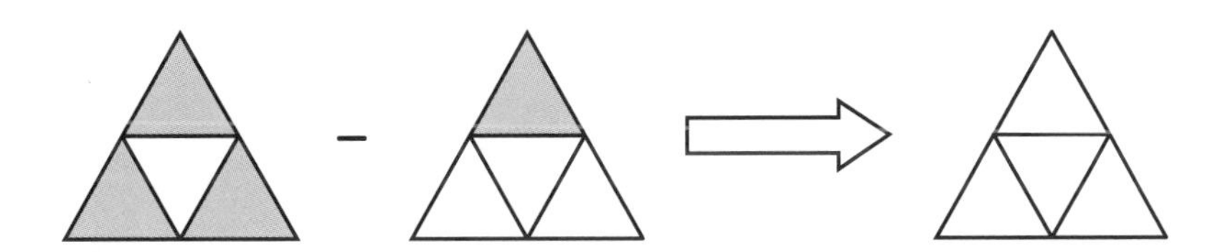

**Subtract.**
**Use models to help you.**

**13.** $1 - \frac{2}{4} =$ __________

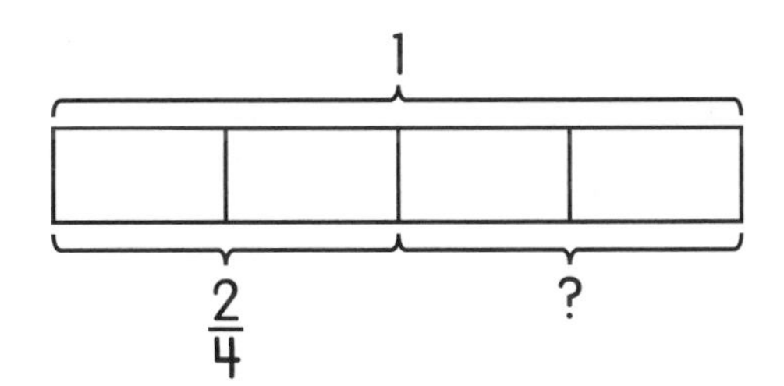

Name: ______________________ Date: ______________

**14.** $\frac{2}{3} - \frac{1}{3} =$ ______

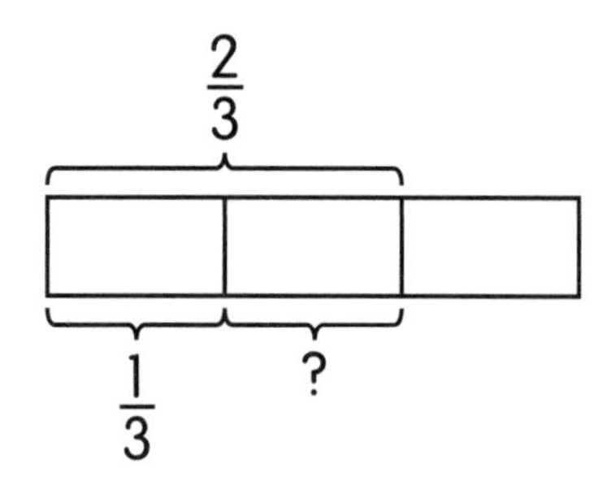


**15.** $1 - \frac{1}{2} =$ ______

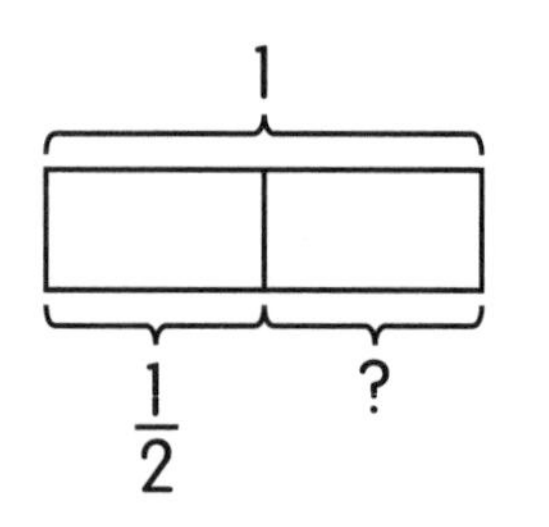


**16.** $\frac{3}{4} - \frac{2}{4} =$ ______

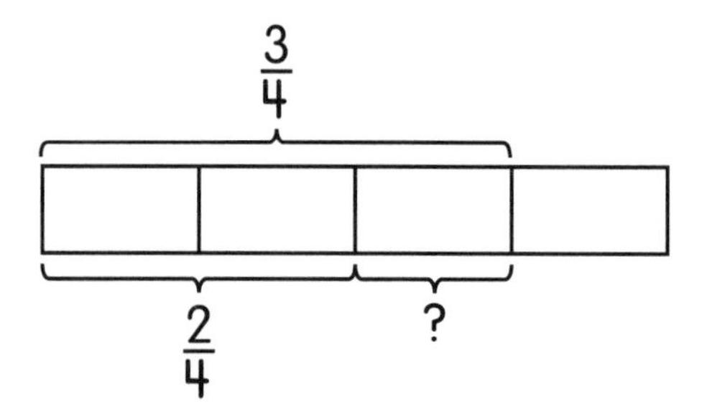

Name: ______________________ Date: ______________

## Put on Your Thinking Cap!

**Solve.**

**1.** A pizza is cut equally into four parts.
Peter takes one-half of the pizza.
He eats $\frac{1}{2}$ of what he takes.

**a.** What fraction of the pizza did he eat?
Color the pizza to show the fraction of pizza eaten by Peter.

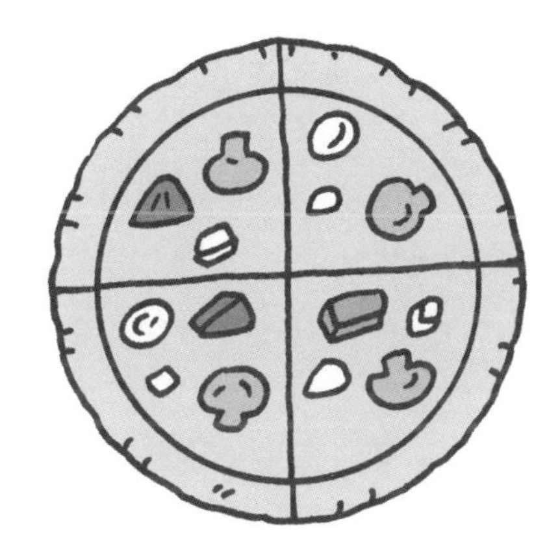

He ate __________ of the pizza.

**b.** What fraction of the pizza is left?

__________ of the pizza is left.

Name: ______________________ Date: ______________

**2.** Paul colors $\frac{1}{4}$ of the stars.

How many more stars must he color so that $\frac{1}{2}$ of the stars are colored?

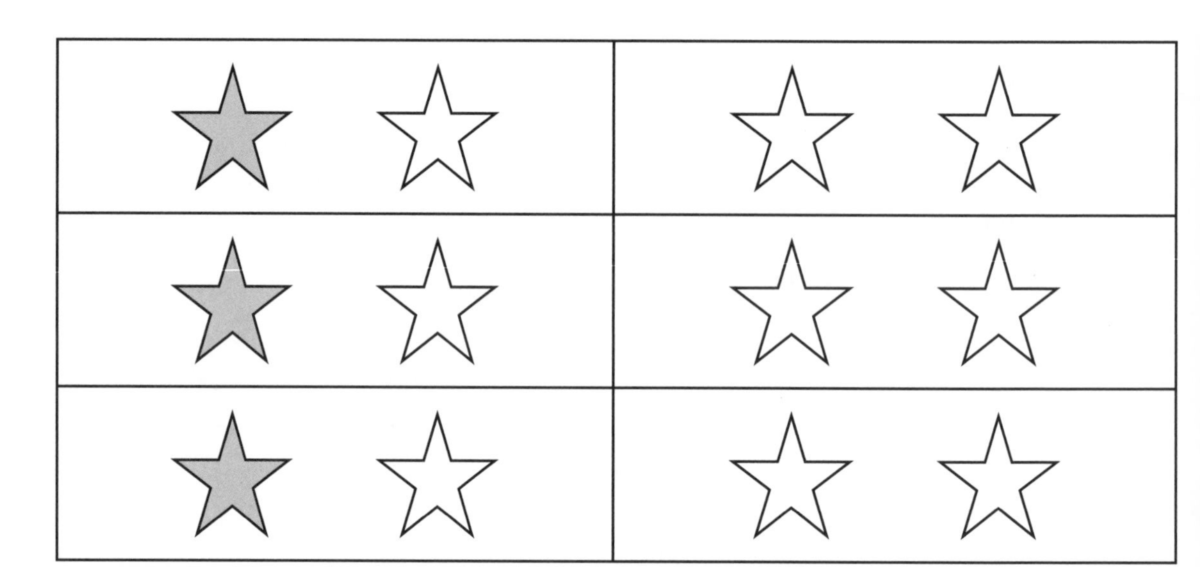

He must color ________ more stars.

Name: ______________________ Date: ______________

# Customary Measurement of Length

## Lesson 1 Measuring in Feet

**Look at the pictures.**
**Fill in the blanks with *more* or *less*.**

**1.**

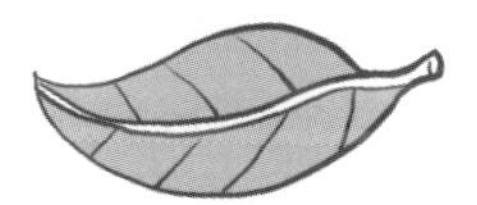

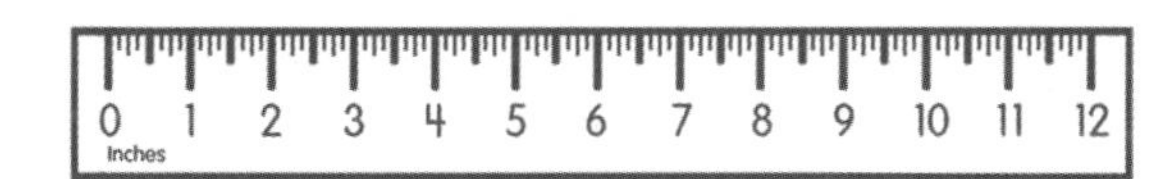


The length of the leaf is ______________ than 1 foot.

**2.**

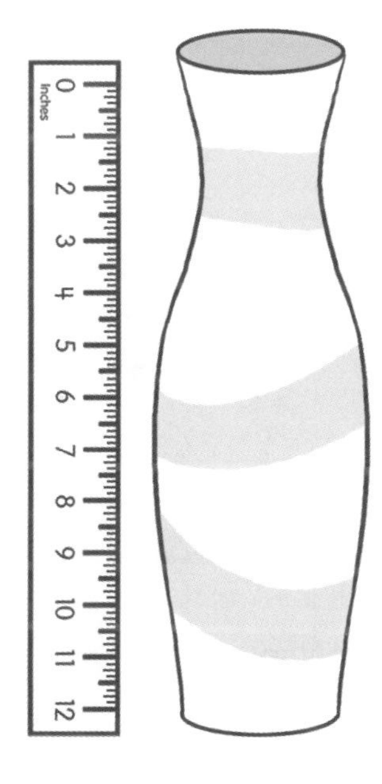


These rulers are smaller than in real life.

The height of the vase is ______________ than 1 foot.

Name: ______________________ Date: ______________

**Look at the list.**
**Check (✓) the columns that are true.**

| Item | Less than 1 foot | More than 1 foot |
|---|---|---|
| 3. Key | | |
| 4. Baseball bat | | |
| 5. Table tennis racket | | |
| 6. Stapler | | |

Name: ______________________ Date: ______________

# Lesson 2 Comparing Lengths in Feet

**Circle the objects that are about a foot long or tall.**

**1.**

calculator

textbook

**2.**

mittens

trash bin

**3.**

toothpaste

handbag

Name: ______________________________ Date: ____________________

**Fill in the blanks.**

**4.** Look at the two pieces of ribbon.

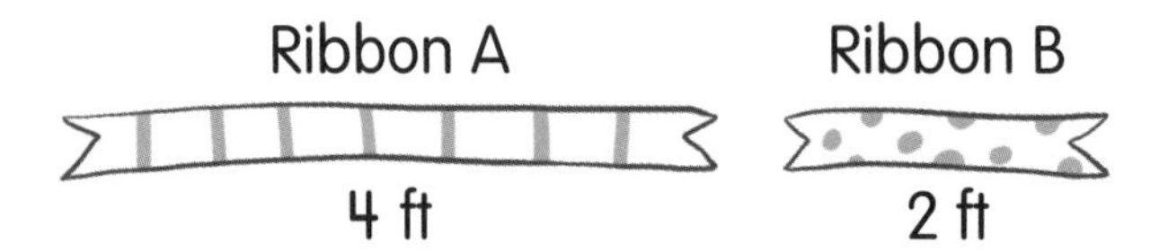


**a.** Which ribbon is longer? Ribbon __________

**b.** How much longer is it? __________ ft

**5.** Look at the three poles.

Pole A : 3 ft

Pole B : 9 ft

Pole C : 8 ft

**a.** Which pole is the longest? Pole __________

**b.** How much longer is Pole C than Pole A? __________ ft

**c.** Pole B is __________ feet longer than Pole A.

Name: ______________________ Date: ______________

# Lesson 3 Measuring in Inches

**Use an inch ruler to measure each pencil.**
**Then answer the questions.**

1. 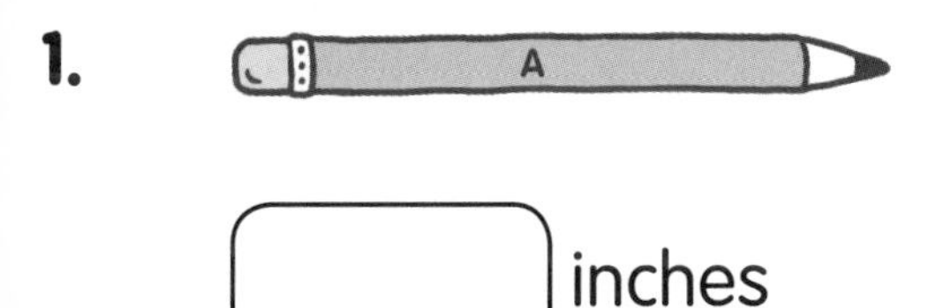


☐ inches

2. 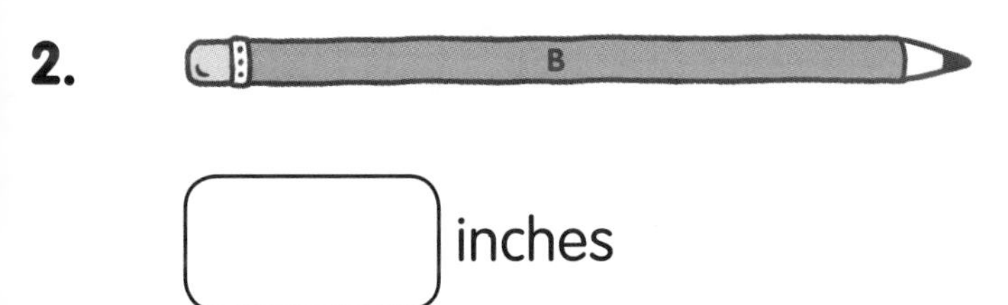


☐ inches

3. 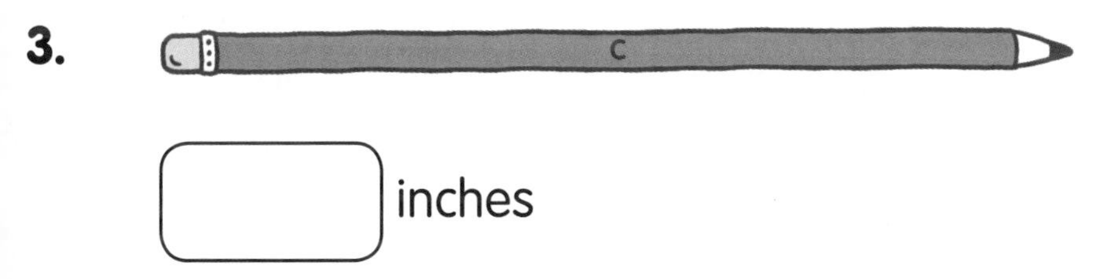


☐ inches

4. 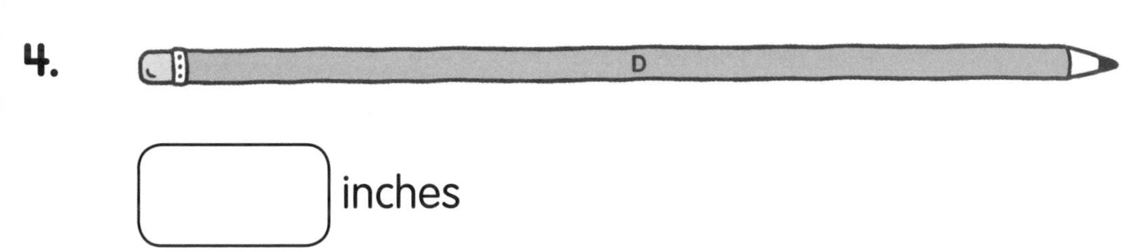


☐ inches

**Use a string and an inch ruler to measure the curve.**

5.

☐ inches

Name: ______________________ Date: ______________

**Fill in the blanks.**

**6.**

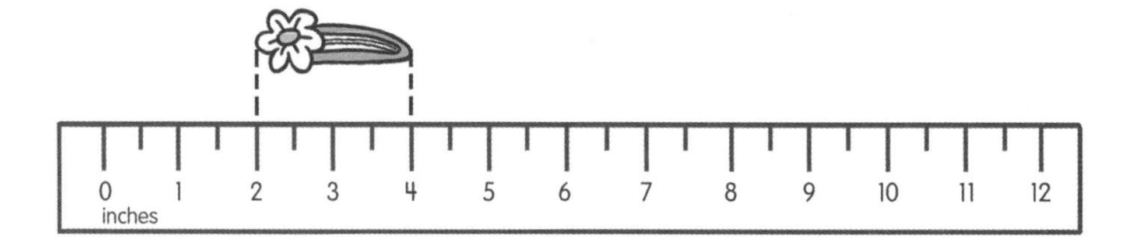


The hair clip is ________ inches long.

**7.**

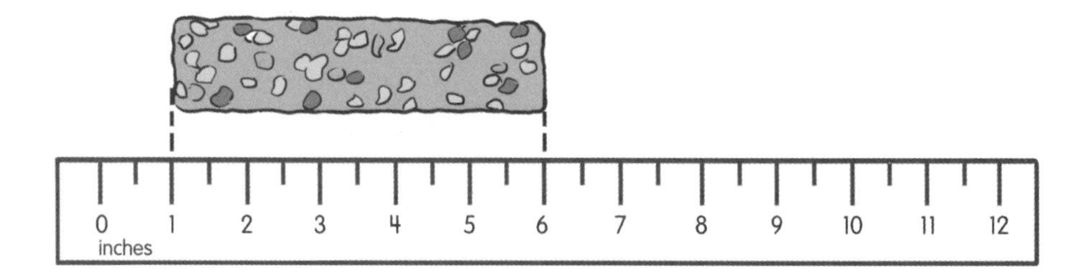


The granola bar is ________ inches long.

**8.**

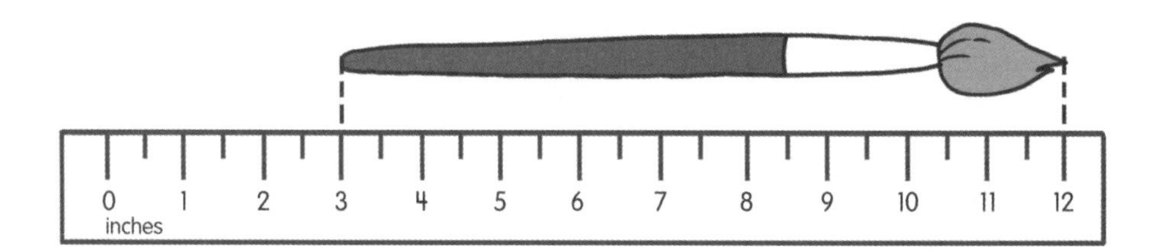


The paintbrush is ________ inches long.

These rulers are smaller than in real life.

Name: ______________________________ Date: ____________________

# Lesson 4 Comparing Lengths in Inches and Feet

**Look at the drawing.**
**Fill in the blanks.**

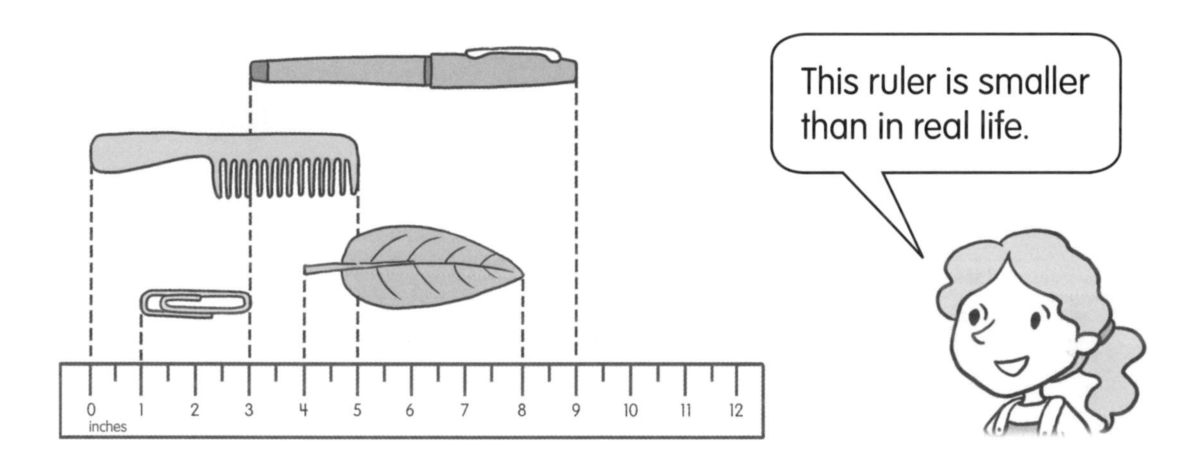


1. The pen is ________ inches long.

2. The comb is ________ inches long.

3. The leaf is ________ inches long.

4. The paper clip is ________ inches long.

**Use your answers for Exercises 1 to 4.**
**Fill in the blanks.**

5. The paper clip is ________ inches shorter than the comb.

6. The pen is ________ inches longer than the leaf.

7. The longest object is the ________________.

8. The shortest object is the ________________.

Name: ______________________ Date: ______________

**Look at the drawing.**
**Fill in the blank.**

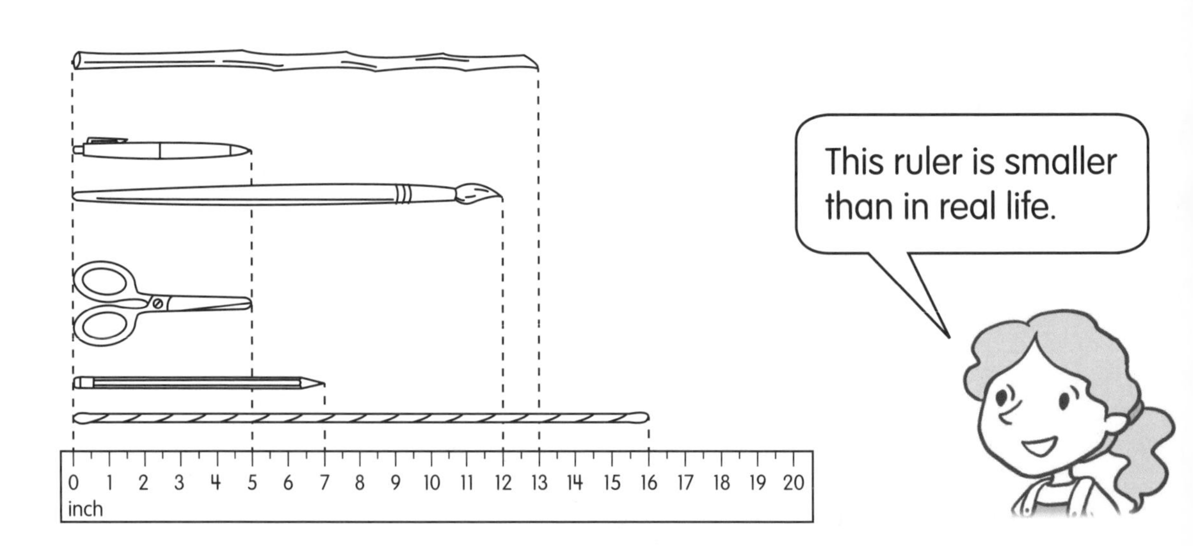


**9.** The pencil is ________ long.

**10.** The scissors are ________ long.

The scissors are the same length as the ________.

**11.** The paint brush is ________ inches long.

It is also ________ foot long.

**12.** The ________ and the ________ are more than 1 foot.

**13.** Order the objects from the shortest to the longest.

________, ________, ________, ________, ________, ________

shortest longest

Name: ______________________ Date: ______________

# Lesson 5 Real-World Problems: Customary Length

**Solve.**

**Use bar models to help you.**

**1.** Shirley buys a piece of lace that is 16 feet long.
She uses 12 feet to make a dress.
What is the length of the lace that she has left?

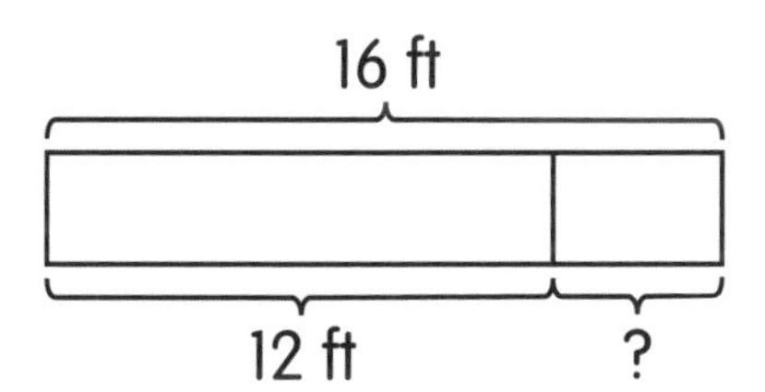


The length of the lace that she has left is ________ feet.

**2.** Tracy has 3 sticks.
Each stick is 9 inches long.
She places all the sticks end to end in a straight line.
What is the total length of the sticks?

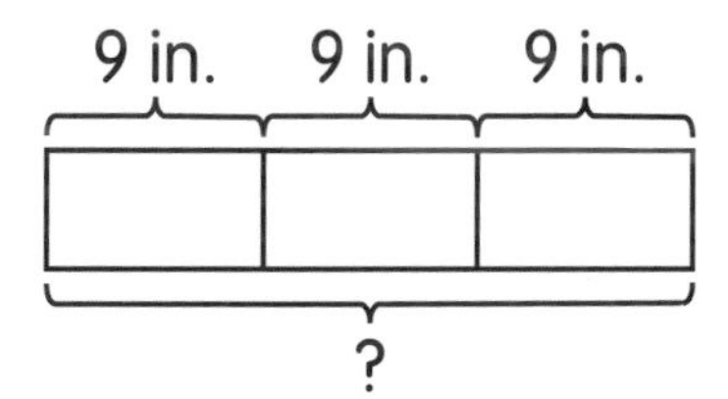


The total length of the sticks is ________ inches.

Name: ______________________ Date: ______________

**Solve.**
**Use bar models to help you.**

**3.** The total length of two jump ropes is 19 feet.
The first jump rope is 8 feet long.

**a.** What is the length of the second jump rope?

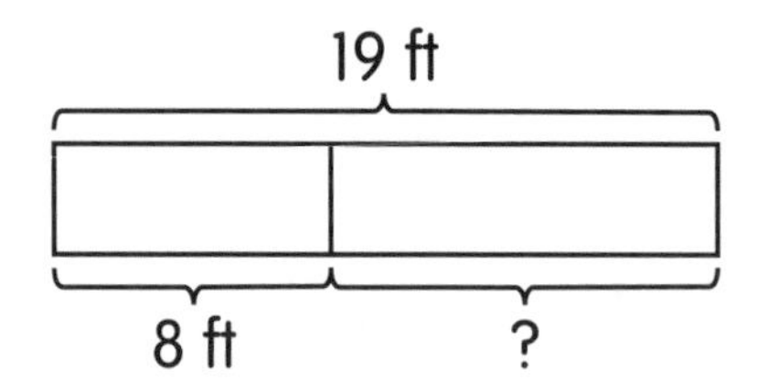


The length of the second jump rope is ________ feet.

**b.** How much longer is the second jump rope than the first jump rope?

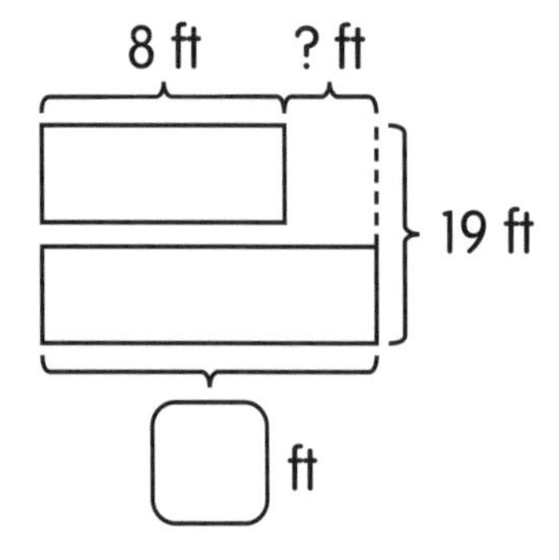


The second jump rope is ________ feet longer than the first jump rope.

Name: ______________________ Date: ______________

**Solve.**
**Draw bar models to help you.**

**4.** Ally buys 15 feet of cloth.
She uses 3 feet of it to sew a cushion cover.
She uses 4 feet of it to sew a tablecloth.
How much cloth does Ally have left?

Ally has ________ feet of cloth left.

**5.** Pete has a string of lights that is 99 inches long.
Sue has a string of lights that is 47 inches long.
How much longer is Pete's string of lights than Sue's string of lights?

Pete's string of lights is ________ inches longer than Sue's string of lights.

Name: ______________________ Date: ______________

# Put on Your Thinking Cap!

**1.** Amy, Sara, Molly, and Jessica each make a necklace. Each necklace is a different length.

**CLUES**

Amy: My necklace is longer than Molly's.
Molly: My necklace is shorter than Jessica's but longer than Sara's.
Jessica: My necklace is shorter than Amy's.

Order the girls by the length of their necklaces from longest to shortest.

__________, __________, __________, __________

longest shortest

Name: ______________________ Date: ______________

# Time

## Lesson 1 The Minute Hand

**Fill in the blanks.**

**1.**

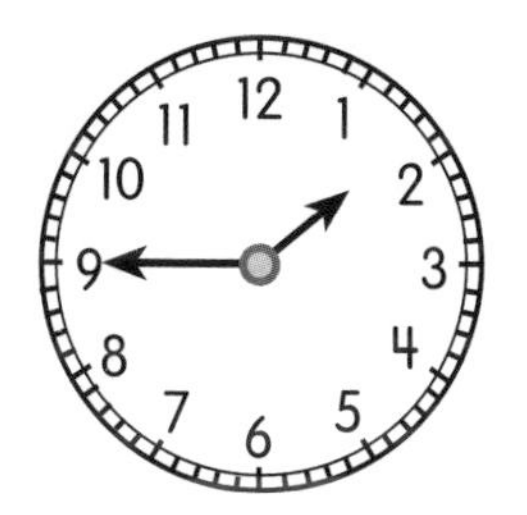


The minute hand points to ________ minutes.

**2.**

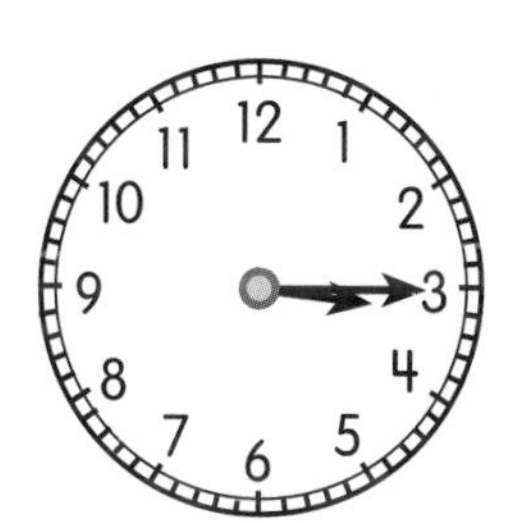


The minute hand points to ________ minutes.

**3.**

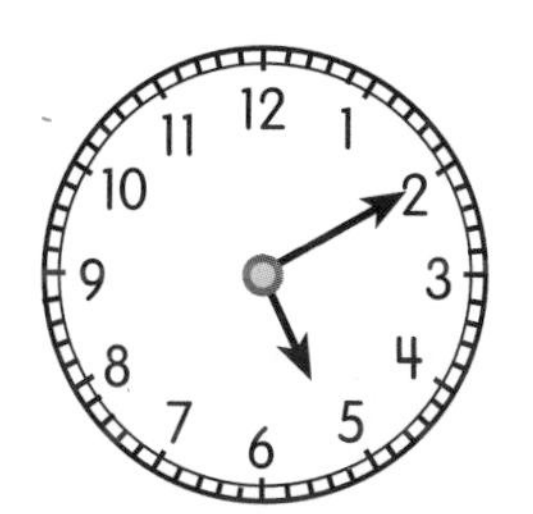


The minute hand points to ________ minutes.

Name: ______________________ Date: ______________

**4.**

The minute hand points to ________ minutes.

**Draw the minute hand to show the time.**

**5.** 20 minutes after 3 o'clock

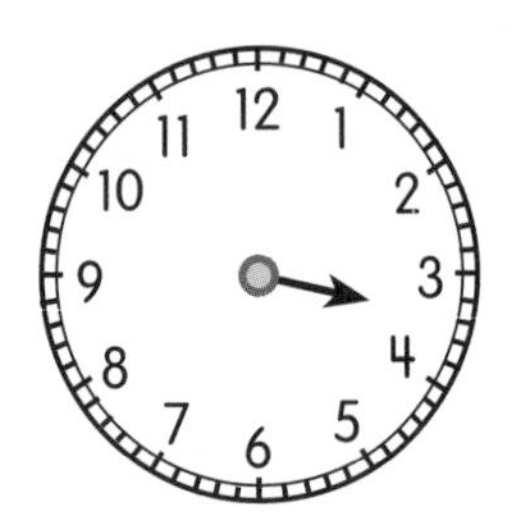

**6.** 30 minutes after 6 o'clock

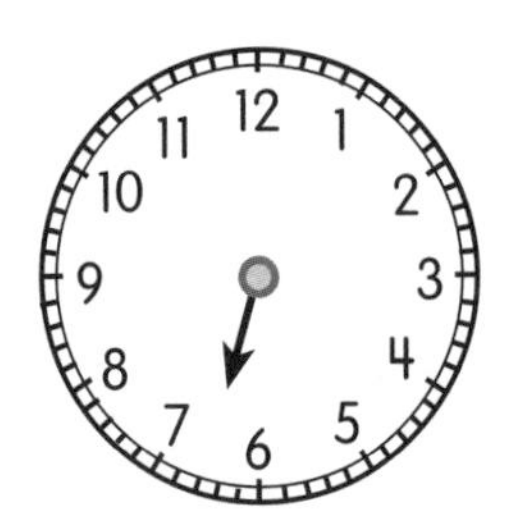

**7.** 55 minutes after 9 o'clock

Name: ______________________ Date: ______________

# Lesson 2 Reading and Writing Time

**Write the time in words.**

1. 

______________________________________

2. 

______________________________________

3. 

______________________________________

4. 

______________________________________

Name: ______________________ Date: ______________

**Write the time in words.**

**5.** 1:30

The time is ______________________.

**6.** 9:35

The time is ______________________.

**7.** 3:40

The time is ______________________.

**8.** 7:55

The time is ______________________.

**Draw the minute hand to show the time.**

**9.**

The time is 7:05.

**10.**

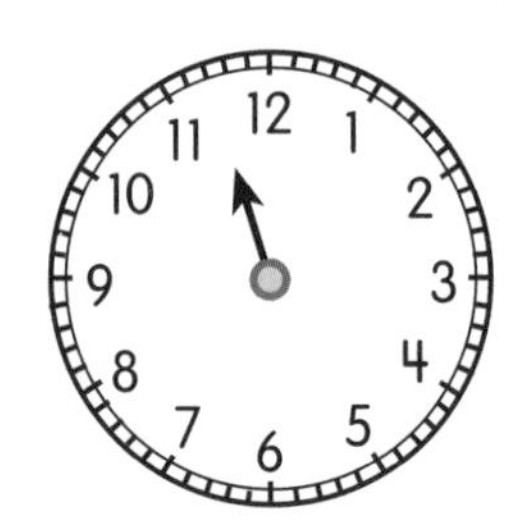


The time is 11:20.

Name: ________________________ Date: ____________

## Draw the hour hand to show the time.

**11.**

The time is 1:00.

**12.**

The time is 8:10.

## Write the time in words.

**13.** 3:15 ______________________________

**14.** 9:20 ______________________________

**15.** 4:30 ______________________________

**16.** 6:45 ______________________________

Name: ______________________ Date: ______________

**Read.**
**Then draw the hands to show the time.**

**17.** Janet left for Welcome Park at **8 o'clock** in the morning.

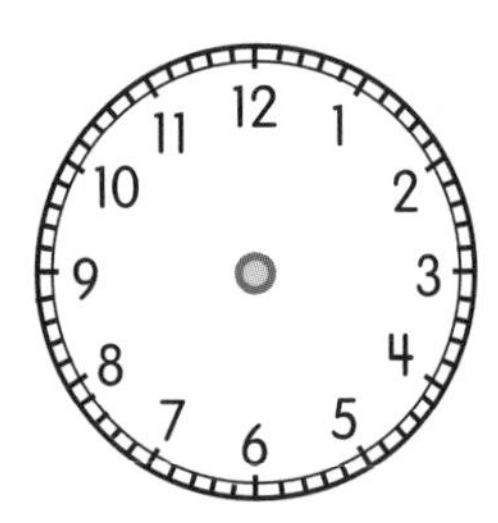

**18.** She reached the park at **9:30** and started jogging.

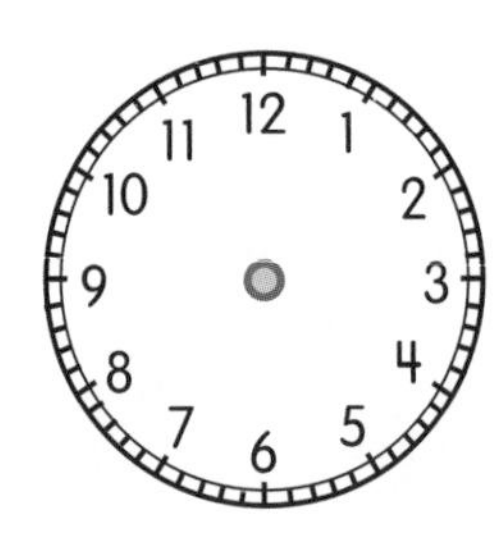

**19.** She left the park at **10:15**.

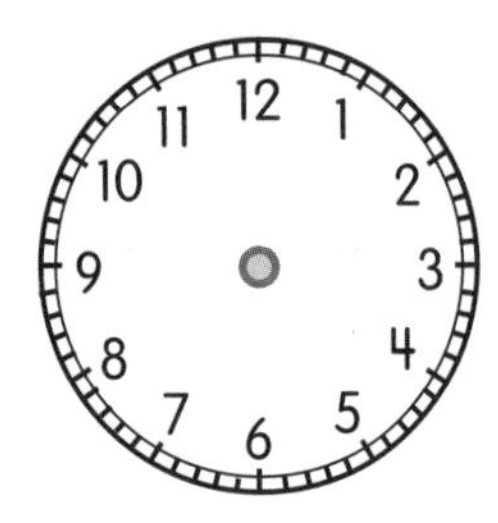

Name: ______________________ Date: ______________

# Lesson 3 Using A.M. and P.M.

**Write A.M. or P.M.**

1. Ten minutes to ten in the evening ________
2. Forty-five minutes after midnight ________
3. Twenty minutes after seven in the morning ________
4. Fifteen minutes after two in the afternoon ________
5. Twenty-five minutes after seven in the evening ________
6. Forty minutes after noon ________

**Write A.M. or P.M.**

7. Andrea does her homework at 8:10 ________ in the evening.
8. Mrs. Lewis jogs in the park at 6:30 ________ in the morning.
9. Jack watches his favorite television show at 5:45 ________ in the evening.
10. Ali walks to school at 7:00 ________ in the morning.

Name: ______________________ Date: ______________

**Look at the pictures.**
**Write the time and A.M. or P.M.**
**Order the events from the beginning of the day by writing 1, 2, 3, 4, 5, and 6 in the boxes.**

**11.**

Name: ______________________ Date: ______________

# Lesson 4 Elapsed Time

**Fill in the blanks with the time.**

**1.**

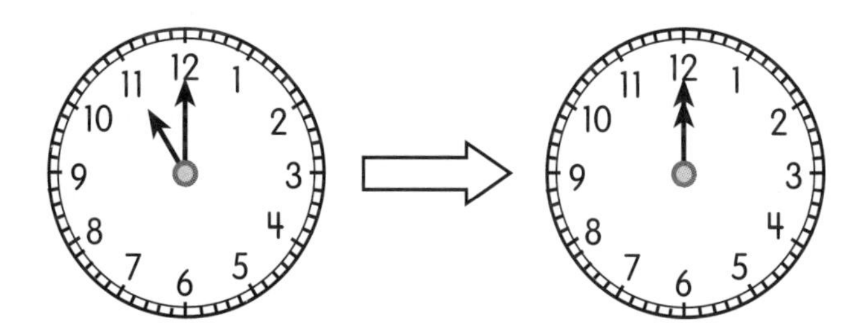

1 hour after 11:00 is ________.

**2.**

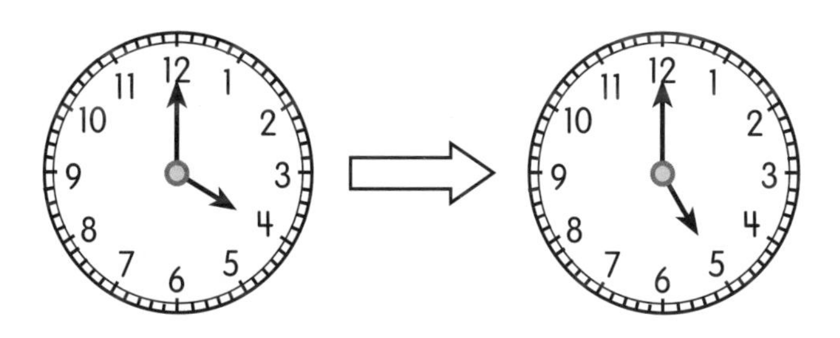

1 hour before 5:00 is ________.

**3.**

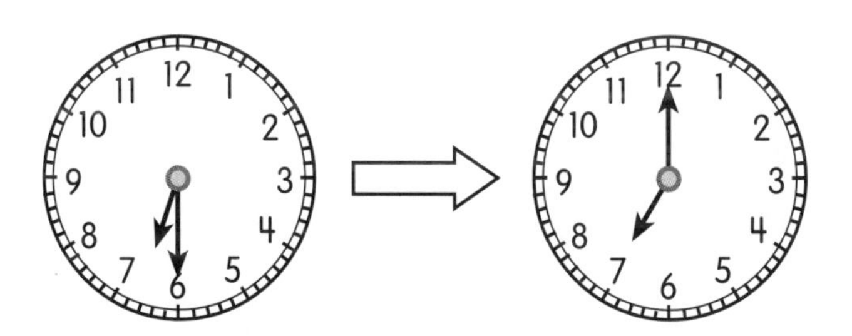

30 minutes after 6:30 is ________.

**4.**

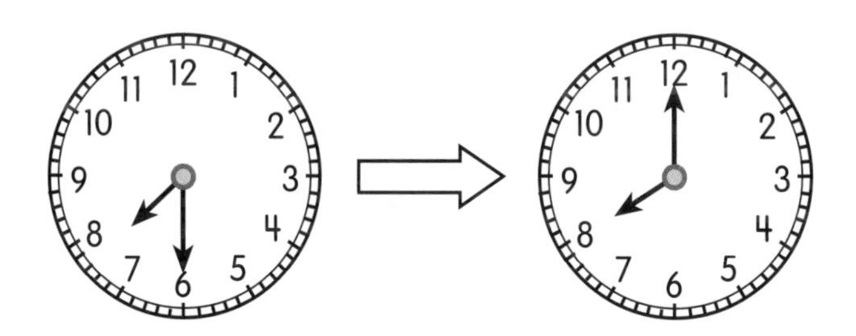

30 minutes before 8:00 is ________.

Name: ____________________ Date: ____________

**Fill in the blanks with the time.**
**Check your answer by drawing the hands on the clock.**

**5.**

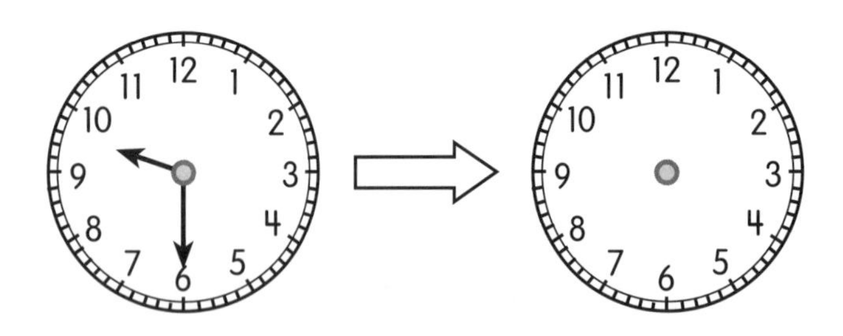

__________ is 1 hour after __________.

**6.**

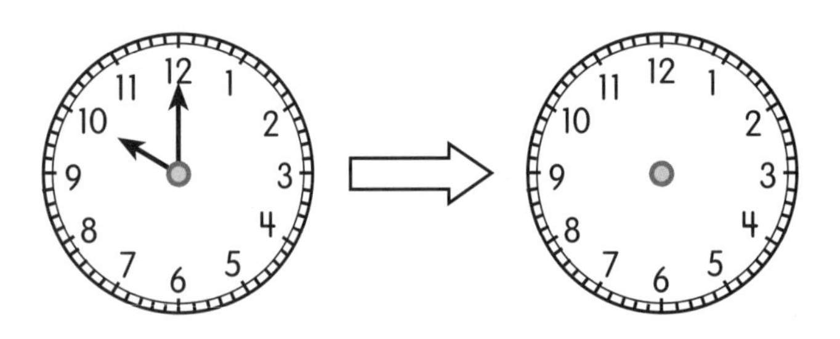

__________ is 1 hour before __________.

**7.**

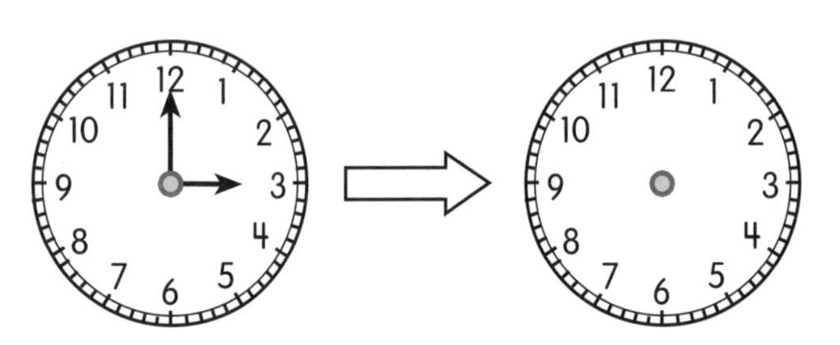

__________ is 30 minutes before __________.

**8.**

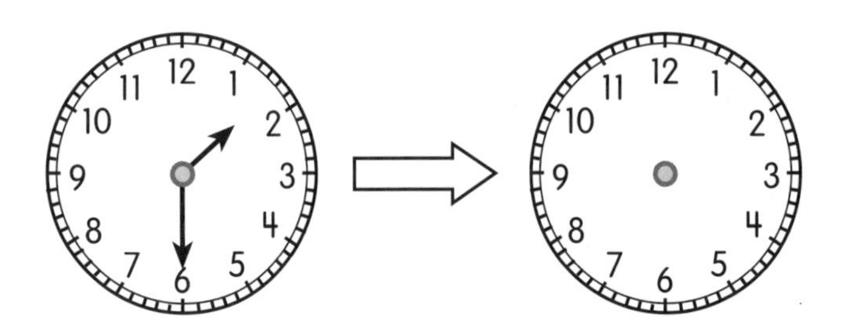

__________ is 30 minutes after __________.

Name: ______________________ Date: ______________

**Draw the hands and write the time.**

**9.** Sandra puts a cake in the oven at 1:30 P.M.
The cake takes 30 minutes to bake.

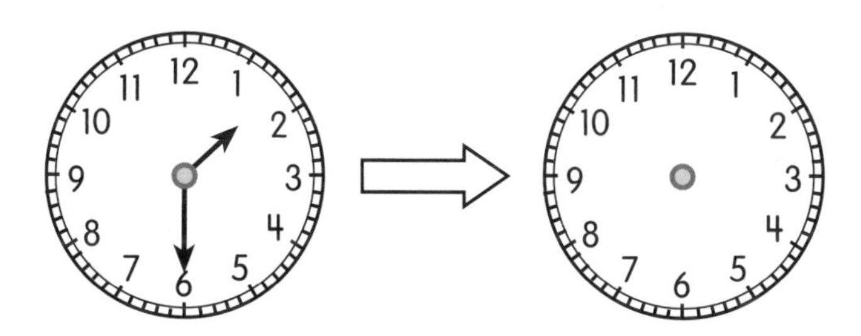

Sandra takes the cake out of the oven at __________ P.M.

**10.** Joel goes to his football practice at 2:00 P.M.
The football practice lasts for 1 hour.

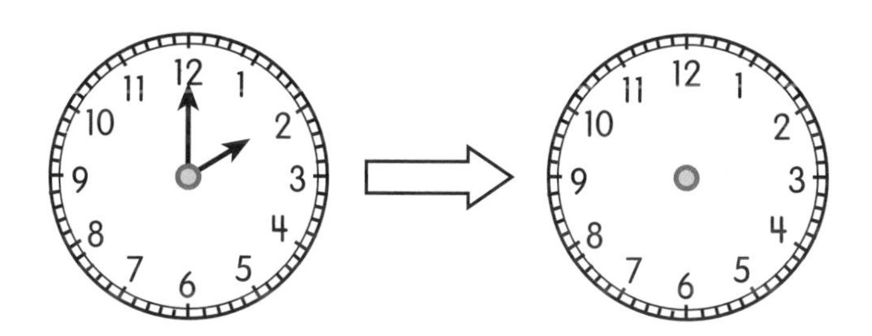

The football practice ends at __________ P.M.

**11.** Julian watches a television program at 8:00 P.M.
The program lasts for 1 hour.

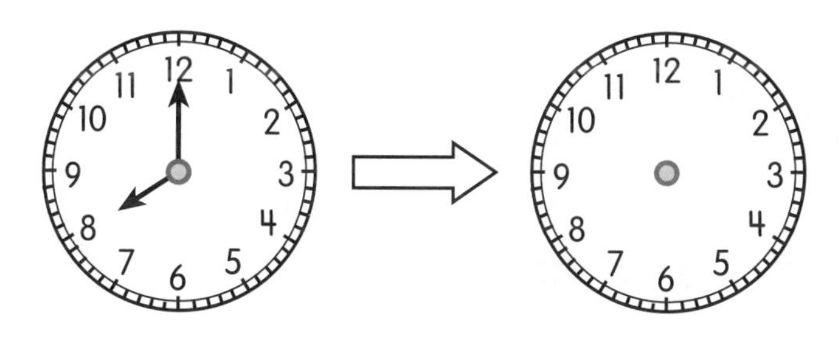

The program ends at __________ P.M.

Name: ______________________ Date: ______________

**Write *before* or *after*.**

12.  is 1 hour ______________ 

13. 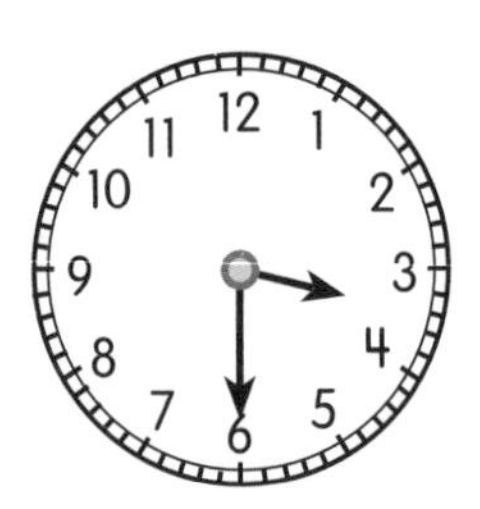 is 1 hour ______________ 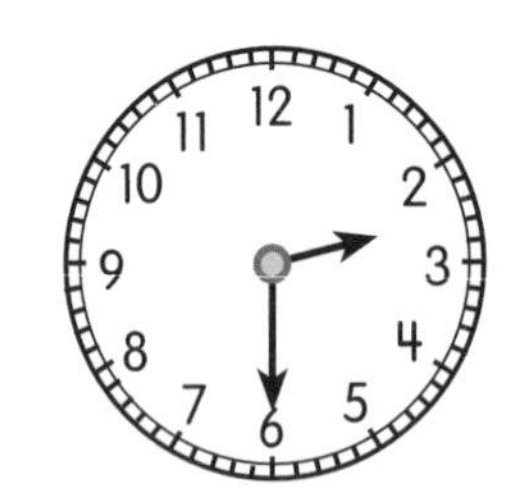

14.  is 30 minutes ______________ 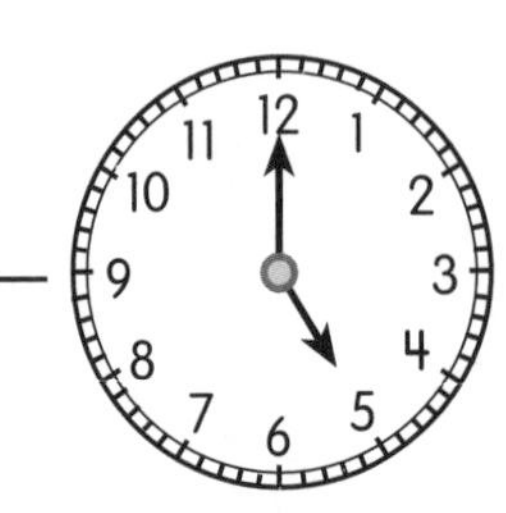

15.  is 30 minutes ______________ 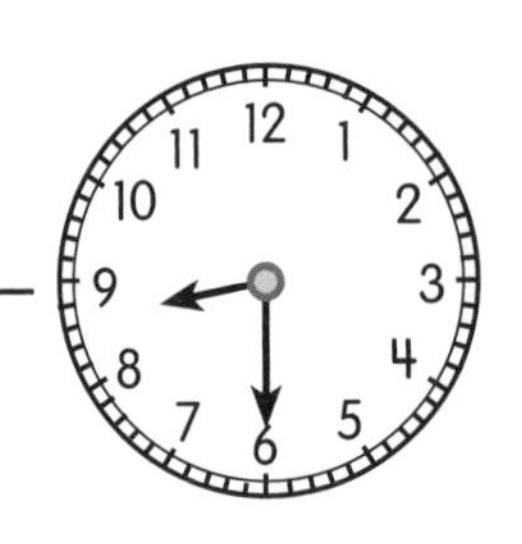

**Fill in the blanks.**

16. Mr. Thomas leaves his home at 7:30 A.M.
He reaches his office at 8 A.M.

He takes __________ minutes to reach his office.

17. The school concert starts at 5 P.M. and ends at 6 P.M.

The concert lasts __________ hour.

Name: ____________________ Date: ____________________

# Put on Your Thinking Cap!

**1.** Jim, Tom, and Ron do their homework.

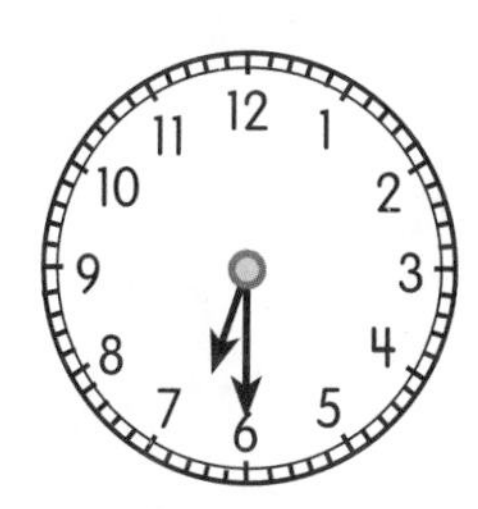


Ron starts doing his homework at 6:30 P.M.
He finishes his homework at 7:30 P.M.

Tom starts doing his homework 30 minutes after Ron.
He finishes it at the same time as Ron.

Jim finishes his homework 1 hour after Ron.
He starts doing it at the same time as Ron.

How long does each boy take to complete his homework?

Name: ________________________ Date: ________________

**Fill in the blanks.**

Jack, Peter, and Sam leave Town A for Town B at the same time.
Jack reaches Town B 2 hours before Sam.
Peter reaches Town B 30 minutes after Sam.
Peter reaches Town B at 9:30 A.M.

**2.** __________ reached Town B first.

**3.** Jack reached Town B at __________.

**4.** Sam reached Town B at __________.

Name: ______________________ Date: ______________

![score box] /50

# Test Prep

## for Chapters 10 to 14

## Multiple Choice (10 × 2 points = 20 points)

**Fill in the circle next to the correct answer.**

**1.** Add 347 to 50 mentally.

The answer is ________.

Ⓐ 297 Ⓑ 352 Ⓒ 397 Ⓓ 847

**2.** Fourteen dollars and five cents can be written as ________.

Ⓐ $145 Ⓑ $14.50 Ⓒ $14.05 Ⓓ 145¢

**3.** Daniel's music lesson starts at 3 P.M. and lasts for 30 minutes. What time will his music lesson end?

Ⓐ 3:25 P.M. Ⓑ 3:30 P.M.

Ⓒ 3:45 P.M. Ⓓ 4:00 P.M.

**4.** ________ + 60 = 292

The missing number is ________.

Ⓐ 232 Ⓑ 258 Ⓒ 350 Ⓓ 358

Name: ________________________ Date: ________________

**5.** Look at the amount of money Sam has.

Which of these toys can he buy with his money?

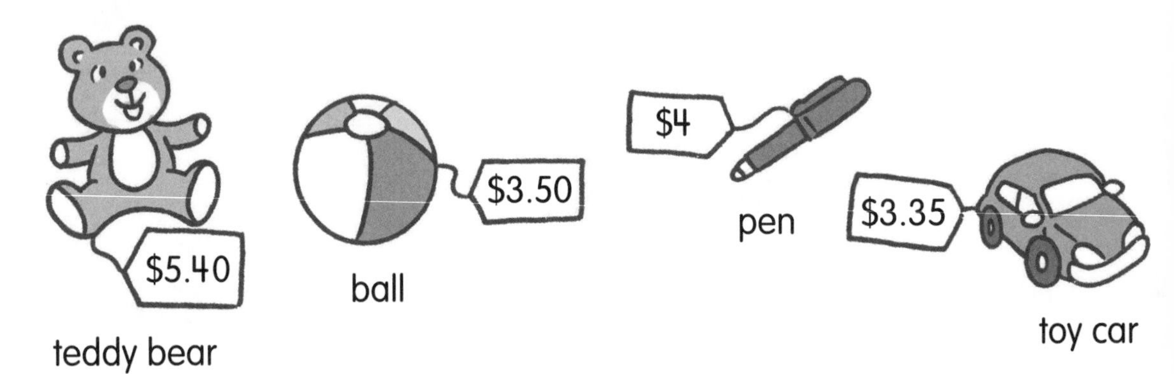


Ⓐ teddy bear Ⓑ ball

Ⓒ pen Ⓓ toy car

**6.** The mat costs __________ more than the basket.

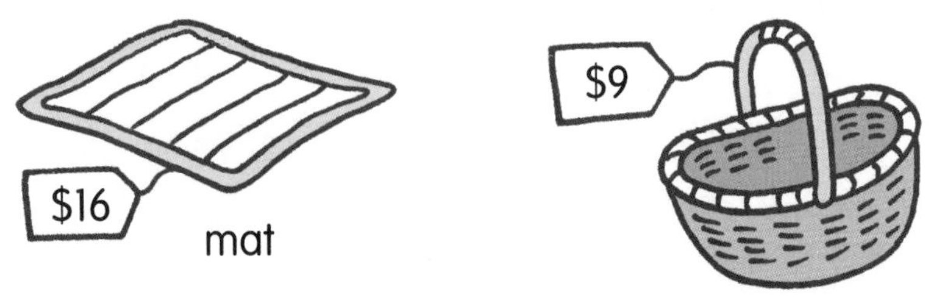


Ⓐ $6 Ⓑ $7 Ⓒ $10 Ⓓ $25

Name: ______________________ Date: ______________

7. Which of the following shows $\frac{3}{4}$ shaded?

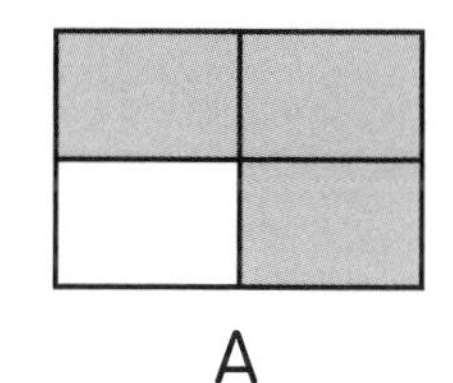

A

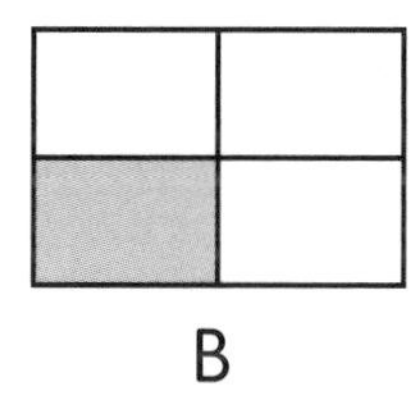

B

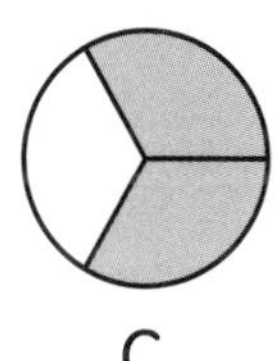

C

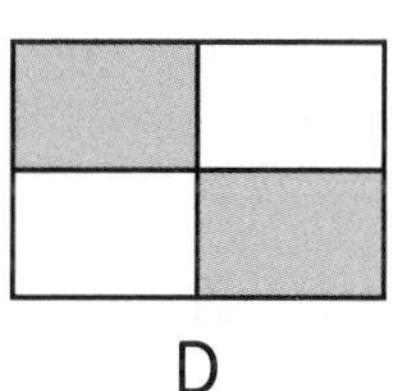

D

Ⓐ A Ⓑ B Ⓒ C Ⓓ D

8. Mrs. Brown cuts a pizza into 4 equal pieces.
Peter eats 2 pieces and David eats 1 piece.
What fraction of the pizza is left?

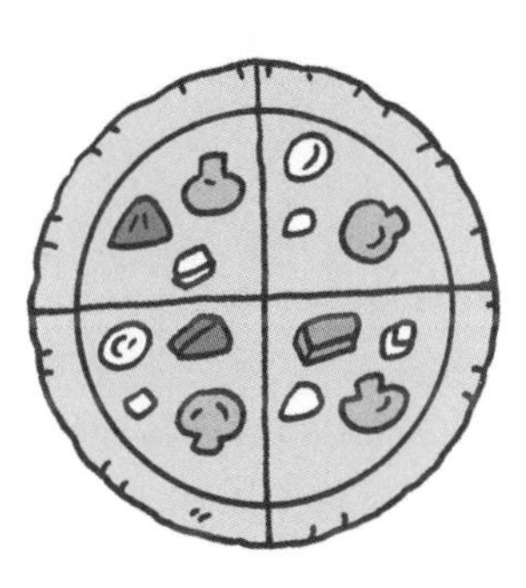

Ⓐ $\frac{1}{2}$ Ⓑ $\frac{1}{4}$ Ⓒ $\frac{3}{4}$ Ⓓ $\frac{2}{4}$

9. Jason reaches his friend's place at 7 P.M.
He stays there for 1 hour.
What time does he leave his friend's place?

Ⓐ 6:30 A.M. Ⓑ 7:30 P.M.

Ⓒ 8:00 P.M. Ⓓ 9:00 P.M.

10. The clock is 30 minutes fast.

The actual time is ________.

Ⓐ 5:30 Ⓑ 5:00 Ⓒ 4:30 Ⓓ 4:00

Name: ______________________ Date: ______________

## Short Answer (10 × 2 points = 20 points)

**Follow the directions.**

**11.** Add or subtract mentally.

**a.** 465 – 9 = ________

**b.** 384 + 8 = ________

**12.** Jenny buys a hotdog and a drink.

**a.** The hotdog costs $________ more than the drink.

**b.** The total cost of the hotdog and the drink is $________.

**13.** Circle the bag that costs more.

Name: ______________________ Date: ______________

**14.** Mrs. Taylor has $45.
She spends $25.

She has $________ left.

**15.**

**16.** Order the fractions from least to greatest.

$\frac{2}{4}$

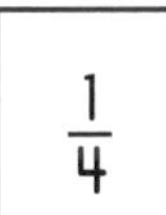


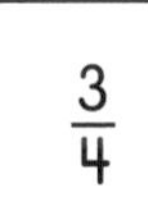


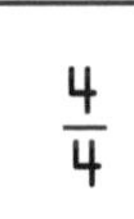


________, ________, ________, ________
least                      greatest

**17.** Draw the hands on the clock to show the time.

The time is 4:50.

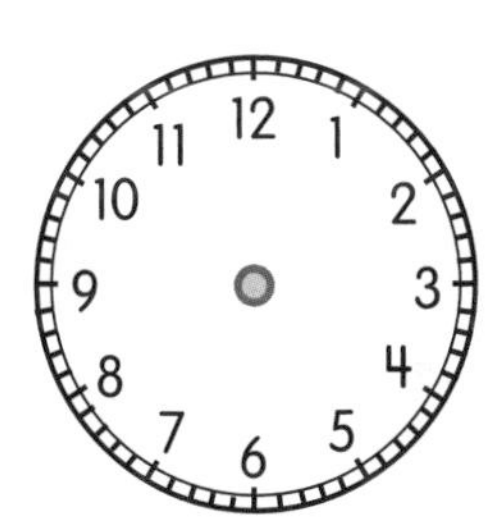

Name: ______________________ Date: ______________

**18.** Amanda starts swimming at 6:30 P.M.
She finishes swimming at 7:00 P.M.

How long did she swim? ________ minutes

**19.** I am thinking of a number.
When I add 30 to it, I get 79.

What is the number? ________

**20.** Circle the bills and coins to show $2.65.

Name: ______________________________ Date: ________________

# Extended Response (8 × 5 points = 40 points)

**Solve.**

**Draw bar models to help you.**

**21.** Marlene buys a bag of apples for $4.50 and a bag of oranges for $5.35.
She gives the cashier $10.
How much change does she get?

She gets $________ in change.

**22.** The Smiths have $400.
They spend $125 on electricity and $49 on groceries.
How much money do they have left?

They have $________ left.

Name: ______________________ Date: ______________

**23.** Nina buys 25 inches of lace.
She uses 18 inches of the lace.
What is the length of the lace she has left?

She has ________ inches of lace left.

**24.** A gardening wire was cut into 3 pieces.
The wire pieces measured 16 feet, 24 feet, and 25 feet.
How long was the wire before it was cut?

The wire was ________ feet long.

Name: ______________________ Date: ______________

**Solve.**
**Show your work.**

**25.** Mrs. Malone reads $\frac{1}{4}$ of a magazine before lunch.
She continues reading the magazine after lunch.
She reads $\frac{3}{4}$ of the magazine in all.
What fraction of the magazine does Mrs. Malone read after lunch? (Show your answer in the model).

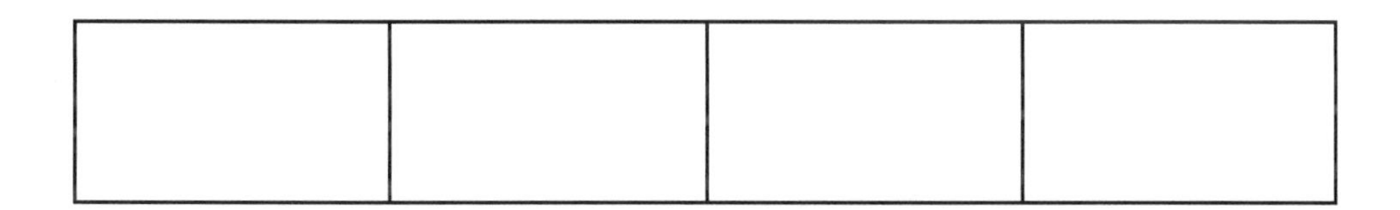

Mrs. Malone reads ________ of the magazine after lunch.

**26.** Anne ate her dinner at 8:00 P.M.
She took 30 minutes to finish her dinner.
What time did she finish her dinner?
Draw the hands on the clock to show your answer.

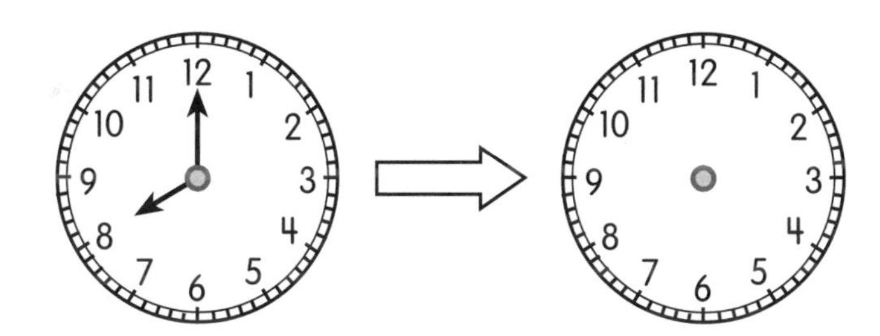


She finished her dinner at ________ P.M.

Name: ______________________ Date: ______________

**Solve.**
**Use bar models to help you.**

**27.** A fencepost is 114 inches tall. After the fencepost is driven into the ground, 33 inches of it is below the ground.
How much of the fencepost is above the ground?

_________ inches of the fencepost is above the ground.

**Add or subtract.**
**Round each number to the nearest ten.**
**Then estimate the sum or difference to check that your answer is reasonable.**

**28.** 445 + 56 = _________

445 is about _________.

56 is about _________.

_________ + _________ = _________

So, 445 + 56 is about _________.

Is the answer reasonable? Explain.

_______________________________________________

_______________________________________________

Name: ______________________ Date: ______________

# Multiplication Tables of 3 and 4

## Lesson 1 Multiplying 3: Skip-Counting

**Count by 3s.**
**Then fill in the blanks.**

**1.** Each tripod has 3 legs.
How many legs do 6 tripods have?

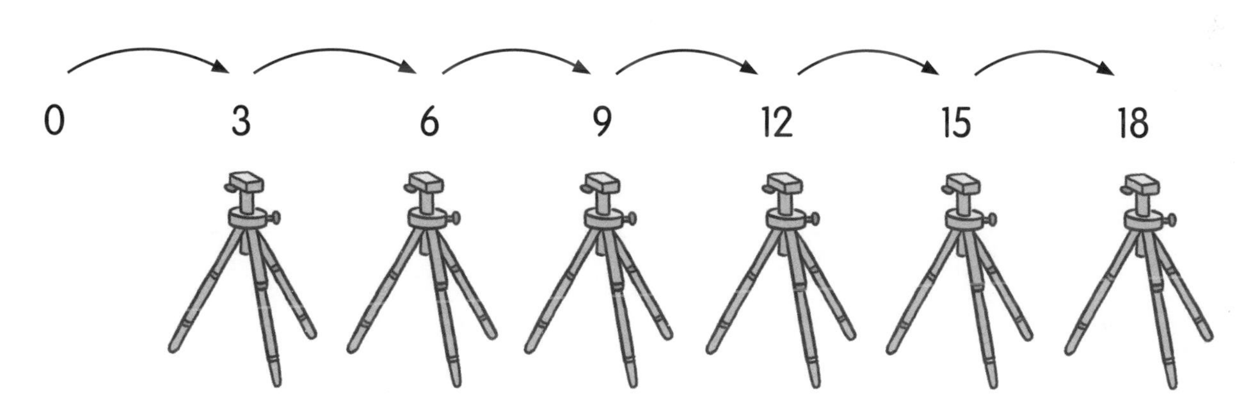


$6 \times 3 =$ ________

6 tripods have ________ legs.

**Use skip-counting to find the missing numbers.**

**2.** 9, ________, ________, ________, 21, 24

**3.** 21, 24, ________, ________, ________, 36

Name: ____________________ Date: ____________

**Find the missing numbers.**

**4.** 5 groups of 3 = ________ × 3

= ________

**5.** 9 groups of 3 = ________ × 3

= ________

**Multiply by 3 to find the missing numbers.**

**6.** 3 × 3 = ________

**7.** 6 × 3 = ________

**8.** 8 × 3 = ________

**9.** 10 × 3 = ________

**Solve.**

**10.** Peter bought 3 jars of jam.
Each jar of jam cost $3.
How much did the jars of jam cost in all?

The jars of jam cost $________ in all.

Name: ______________________ Date: ______________

**11.** There are 7 boxes.
Each box has 3 pencils in it.
How many pencils are there in all?

There are ________ pencils in all.

**12.** There are 9 shelves on a bookshelf.
Each shelf has 3 books on it.
How many books are there in all?

There are ________ books in all.

Name: ______________________ Date: ______________

**13.** Angie has 7 pouches.
Each pouch has 3 bracelets.
How many bracelets are there in all?

There are ________ bracelets in all.

**14.** A pet shop has 10 fish tanks.
Each fish tank has 3 fish.
How many fish are there in all?

There are ________ fish in all.

Name: ______________________ Date: ______________

# Lesson 2 Multiplying 3: Using Dot Paper

**Use dot paper to solve.**

**1.** There are 5 cakes.
Each cake is cut into 3 pieces.
How many pieces of cake are there in all?

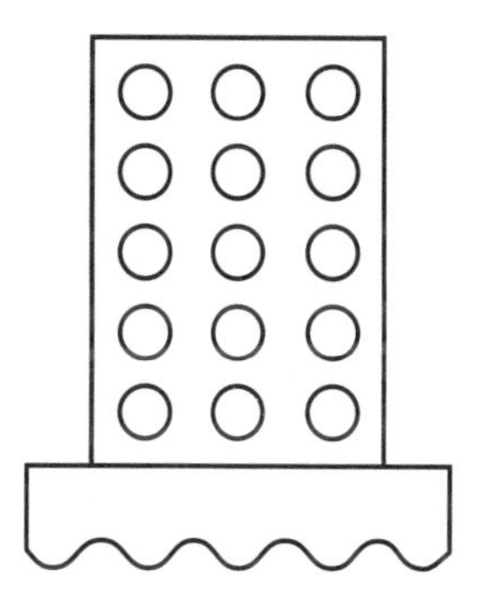

There are ________ pieces of cake in all.

**2.** There are 7 children.
Each child has 3 granola bars.
How many granola bars do they have in all?

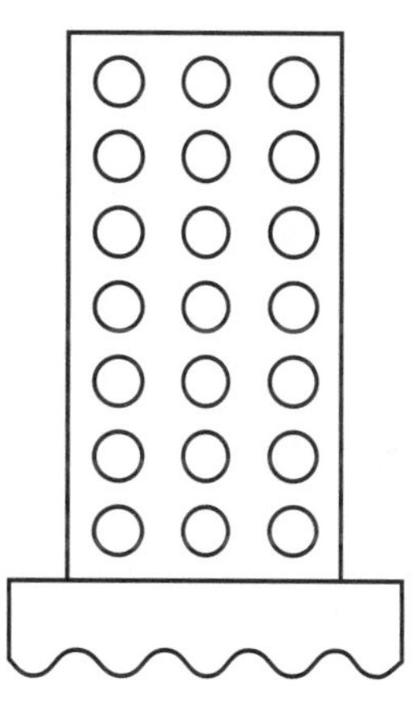

They have ________ granola bars in all.

Name: _______________ Date: _______________

**3.** Jolere bakes 3 muffins.
She cuts each muffin into 3 pieces.
How many pieces of muffin are there in all?

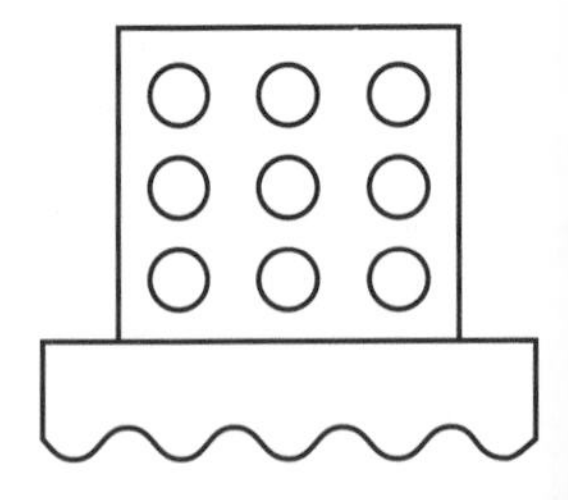

There are ________ pieces of muffin in all.

**4.** There are 8 key chains.
Each key chain has 3 keys.
How many keys are there in all?

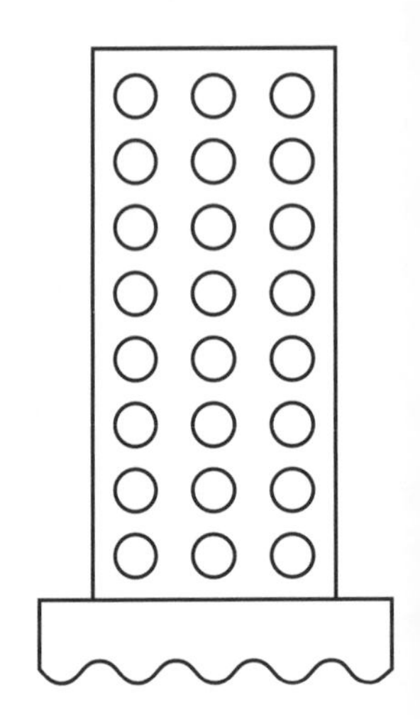

There are ________ keys in all.

Name: ______________________ Date: ______________

## Use dot paper to help you match.

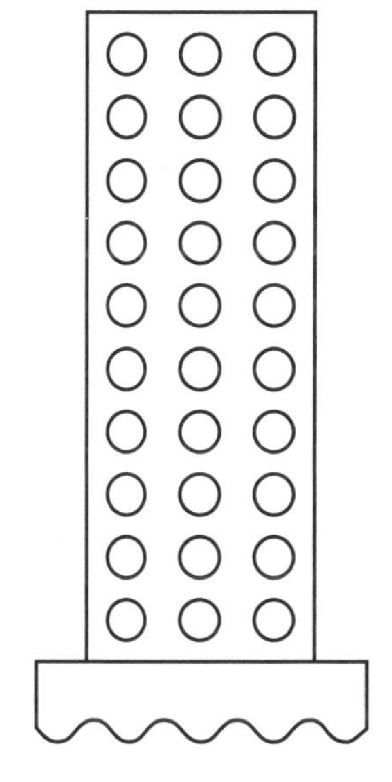

| | | | |
|---|---|---|---|
| **5.** | $6 \times 3$ • | • $27 + 3$ |
| **6.** | $8 \times 3$ • | • $15 + 3$ |
| **7.** | $10 \times 3$ • | • $30 - 3$ |
| **8.** | $9 \times 3$ • | • $30 - 6$ |

## Use facts you know to find the missing numbers.

**9.** $9 \times 3 = ?$

Start with 10 groups of 3.

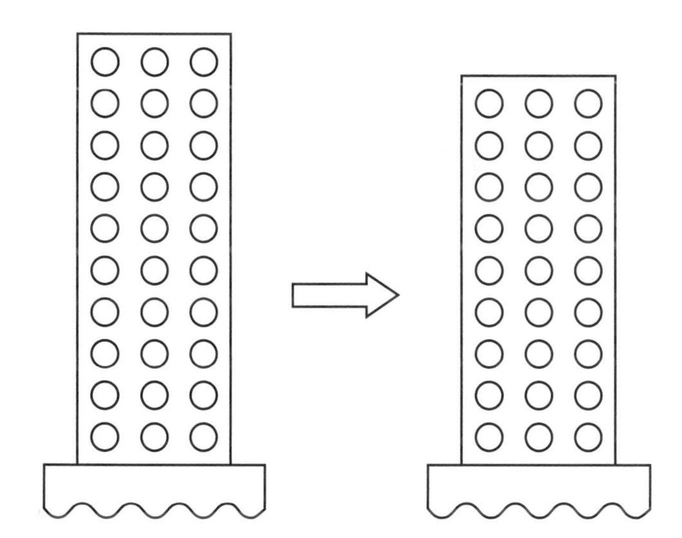

$10 \times 3 =$ ________ $9 \times 3 =$ 10 groups of 3 – 1 group of 3

= ________ – ________

= ________

Name: ______________________ Date: ______________

**10.** $7 \times 3 = 5$ groups of 3 + 2 groups of 3

$= \_\_\_\_\_\_ + \_\_\_\_\_\_$

$= \_\_\_\_\_\_$

**Use dot paper to find the missing numbers.**

**11.** $4 \times 3 = \_\_\_\_\_\_$ $3 \times 4 = \_\_\_\_\_\_$

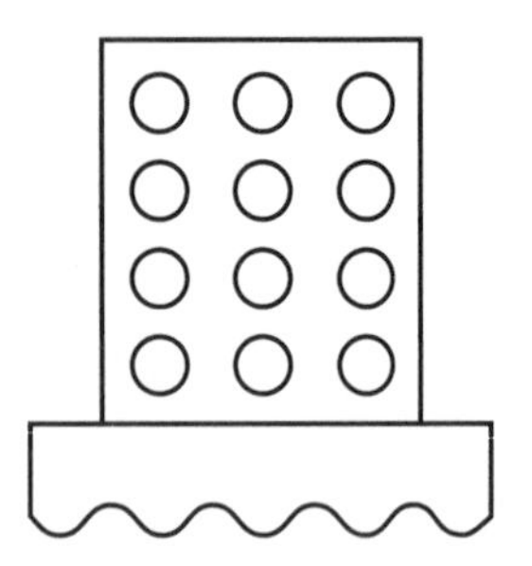

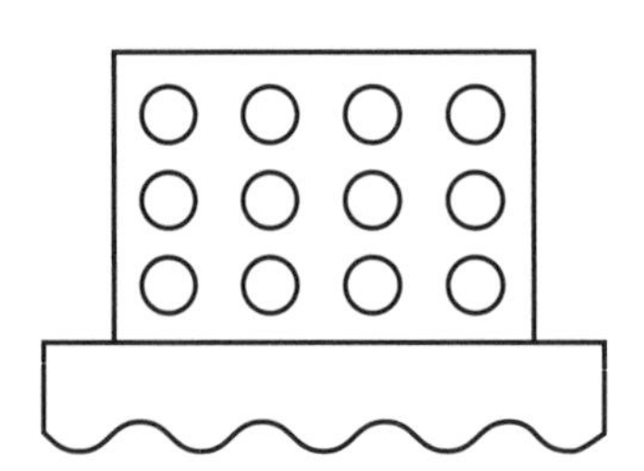

**12.** $8 \times 3 = \_\_\_\_\_\_$ $3 \times 8 = \_\_\_\_\_\_$

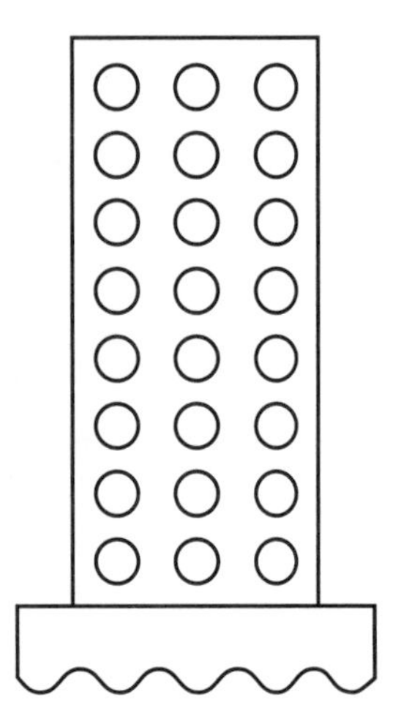

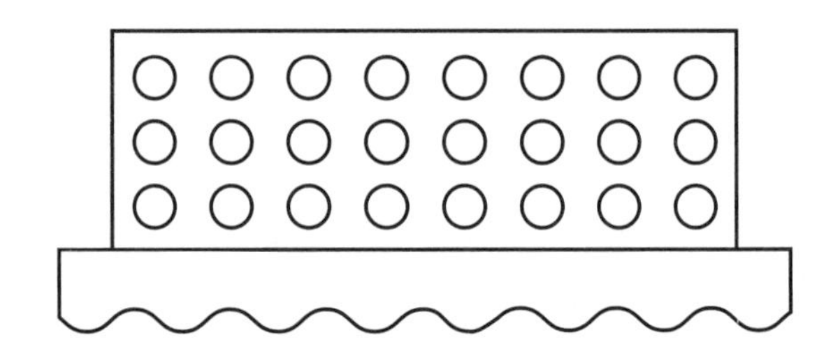

Name: ______________________ Date: ______________

# Lesson 3 Multiplying 4: Skip-Counting

**Count by 4s.**
**Fill in the blanks.**

**1.** ________, 12, 16, ________, ________, 28, ________

**2.** ________, 20, ________, ________, 32, ________, 40

**Use skip-counting to find the missing numbers.**

**3.**

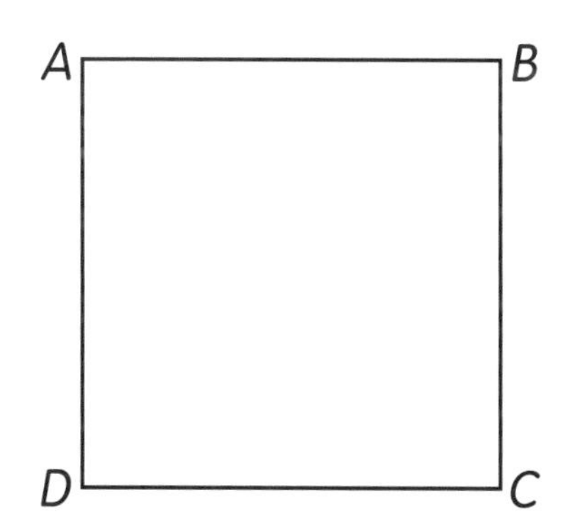

| Number of squares | 1 | 2 | 3 | 4 | 5 | 6 | 7 | | | 10 |
|---|---|---|---|---|---|---|---|---|---|---|
| Number of sides | 4 | | 12 | | | | | 32 | 36 | |

Name: ______________________ Date: ______________

**Solve.**

**4.** There are 4 stickers on one sheet.
There are 4 sheets of stickers.
How many stickers are there in all?

$4 \times 4 =$ ________

There are ________ stickers in all.

**5.** Mrs. Ross buys 6 T-shirts.
Each T-shirt costs $4.
How much do the T-shirts cost in all?

$6 \times 4 =$ ________

The T-shirts cost $________ in all.

Name: ______________________ Date: ______________

# Lesson 4 Multiplying 4: Using Dot Paper

**Use dot paper to solve.**

**1.** There are 5 bags of marbles.
Each bag has 4 marbles.
How many marbles are there in all?

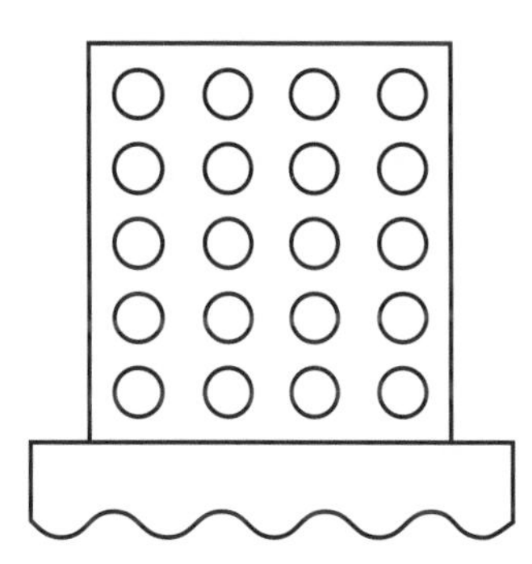

$5 \times 4 =$ ________

There are ________ marbles in all.

**2.** Peter, Jack, and Sam are Mrs. Hill's children.
She gives each child 4 cookies.
How many cookies does she give in all?

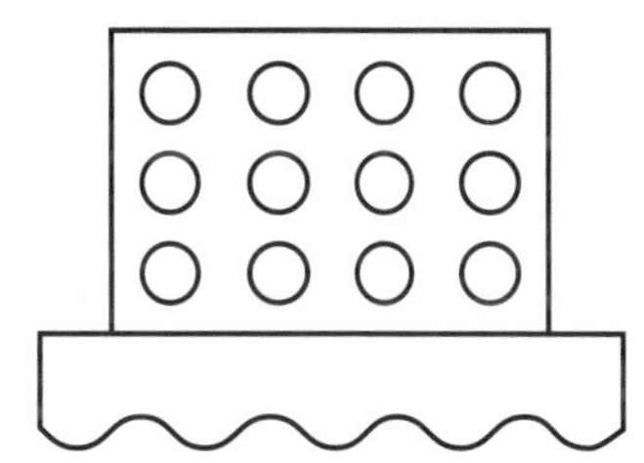

She gives ________ cookies in all.

Name: ______________________ Date: ______________

**3.** Mrs. Turner buys 8 shirts.
Each shirt has 4 buttons.
How many buttons are there in all?

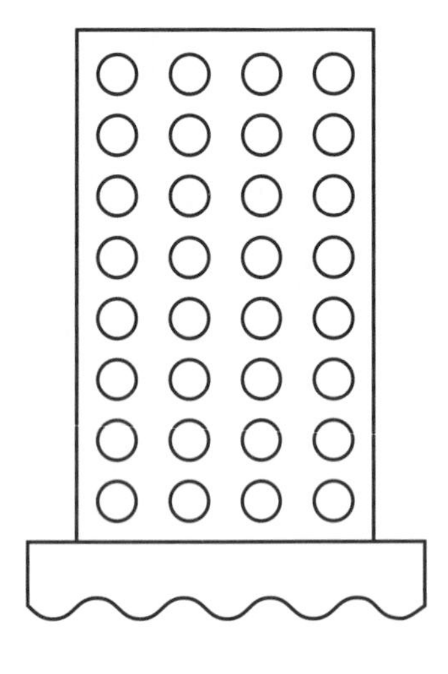

There are ________ buttons in all.

**4.** Mr. Vasquez uses 4 flowers to make each lei.
He makes 10 leis.
How many flowers does Mr. Vasquez use in all?

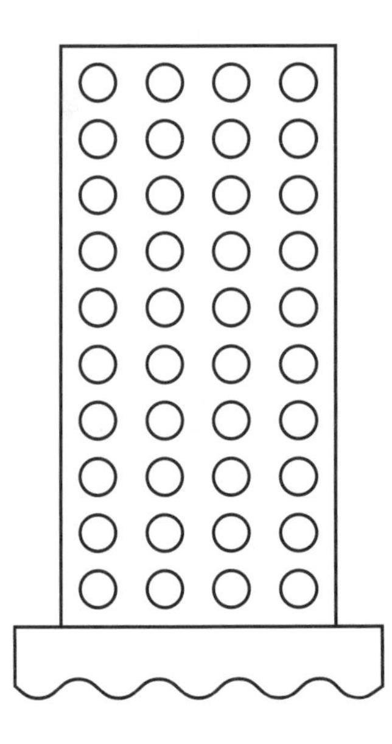

Mr. Vasquez uses ________ flowers in all.

Name: ______________________ Date: ______________

**Use facts you know to find the missing numbers.**

**5.** $8 \times 4 = ?$

Start with 10 groups of 4.

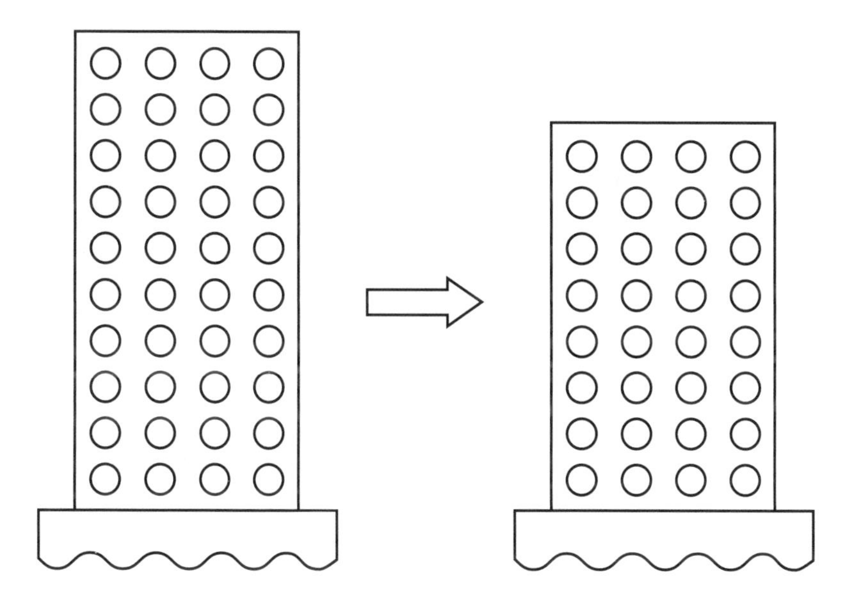

$10 \times 4 =$ ______

$8 \times 4 =$ 10 groups of 4 – 2 groups of 4

= ______ – ______

= ______

**6.** $6 \times 4 =$ 5 groups of 4 + 1 group of 4

= ______ + ______

= ______

Name: ____________________ Date: ____________

## Use dot paper to find the missing numbers.

**7.** $2 \times 4 =$ ______ $4 \times 2 =$ ______

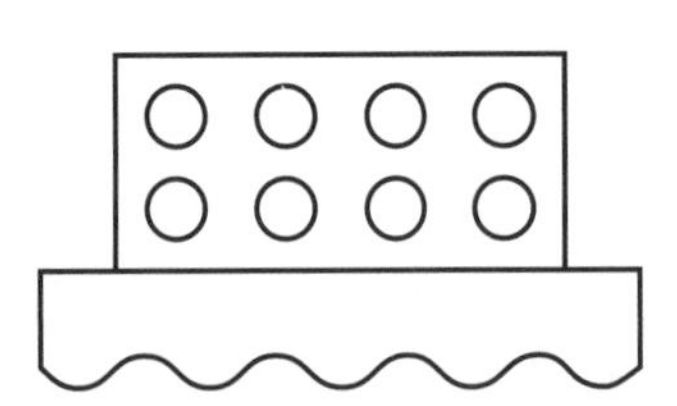

**8.** $9 \times 4 =$ ______ $4 \times 9 =$ ______

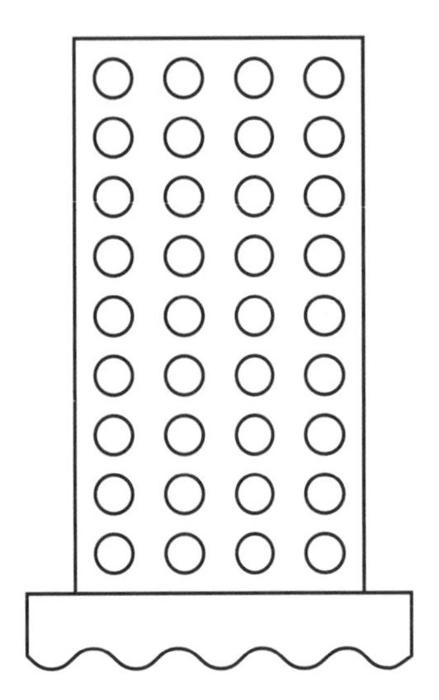

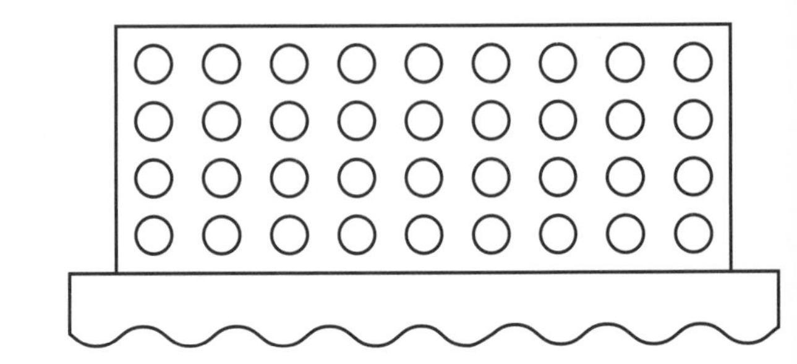

Name: ______________________ Date: ______________

# Lesson 5 Divide Using Related Multiplication Facts

**Find the missing numbers.**
**Use related multiplication facts to help you divide.**

**1.** Divide 16 bones into 2 equal groups.
How many bones are there in each group?

$2 \times$ ________ $= 16$

So, $16 \div 2 =$ ________

There are ________ bones in each group.

**2.** Divide 21 birds into 3 equal groups.
How many birds are there in each group?

$3 \times$ ________ $= 21$

So, $21 \div 3 =$ ________

There are ________ birds in each group.

Name: ____________________ Date: ____________

**Find the missing numbers.**
**Then write three related number sentences.**
**Write one multiplication sentence and two division sentences.**

**3.** $5 \times 3 =$ ______

$3 \times 5 =$ ______

______ $\div 3 =$ ______

______ $\div 5 =$ ______

**4.** $5 \times 4 =$ ______

$4 \times 5 =$ ______

______ $\div 4 =$ ______

______ $\div 5 =$ ______

**Use the numbers below to form multiplication and division sentences.**

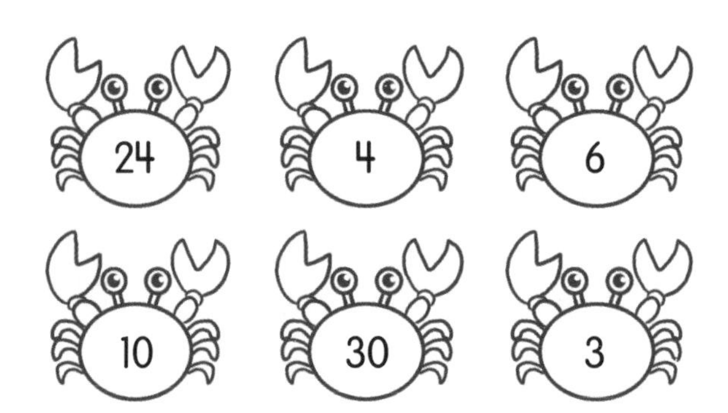


**5.** ______ × ______ = ______ ______ × ______ = ______

______ ÷ ______ = ______ ______ ÷ ______ = ______

**6.** ______ × ______ = ______ ______ × ______ = ______

______ ÷ ______ = ______ ______ ÷ ______ = ______

Name: ______________________ Date: ______________

**Find the missing numbers.**
**Then write three related number sentences.**
**Write one multiplication sentence and two division sentences.**

**7.** $6 \times 3 =$ ______

______ × ______ = ______

______ ÷ ______ = ______

______ ÷ ______ = ______

**8.** $9 \times 4 =$ ______

______ × ______ = ______

______ ÷ ______ = ______

______ ÷ ______ = ______

**Use related multiplication facts to solve.**

**9.** Divide 24 muffins equally among 4 boys.
How many muffins does each boy get?

Each boy gets ______ muffins.

**10.** Danny has 27 apples.
He puts 3 apples on each plate.
How many plates are there?

There are ______ plates.

**11.** The science teacher gives out 40 leaves to her students.
Each student gets 4 leaves.
How many students are there?

There are ______ students.

Name: ______________________ Date: ______________

1. Circle all the numbers that can be exactly divided by 3.

| | | | |
|---|---|---|---|
| 24 | 12 | 21 | 5 |
| 13 | 30 | 27 | 18 |
| 16 | 23 | 10 | 29 |
| 15 | 25 | 8 | 9 |

Add the digits of each number that you circled.

What do you notice about each sum?

______________________________________________

Name: ____________________ Date: ____________

# Using Bar Models: Multiplication and Division

## Lesson 1 Real-World Problems: Multiplication

**Solve.**
**Use bar models to help you.**

1. May puts stamps on 5 envelopes.
   She puts 4 stamps on each envelope.
   How many stamps does she put on envelopes in all?

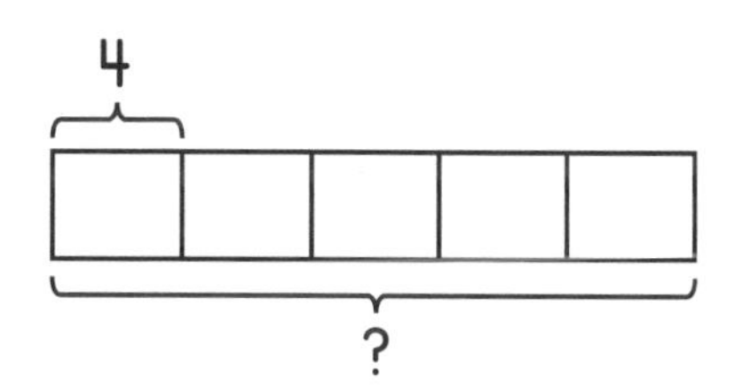


_______ x 4 = _______

She puts _______ stamps on envelopes in all.

2. There are 6 rose bushes in Amy's garden.
   There are 3 roses on each bush.
   How many roses are there in all?

3

?

_______ x 3 = _______

There are _______ roses in all.

Name: ______________________ Date: ______________

**3.** Suzanne does 10 exercises each day.
How many exercises does she do in 5 days?

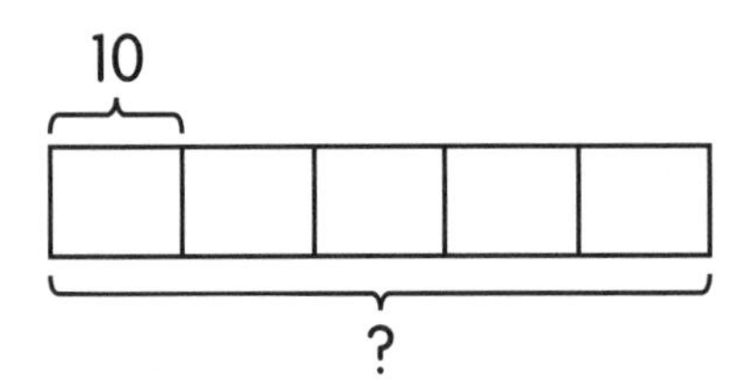


She does ________ exercises in 5 days.

**4.** Colleen has 10 boxes of pencils.
Each box has 4 pencils.
How many pencils does Colleen have in all?

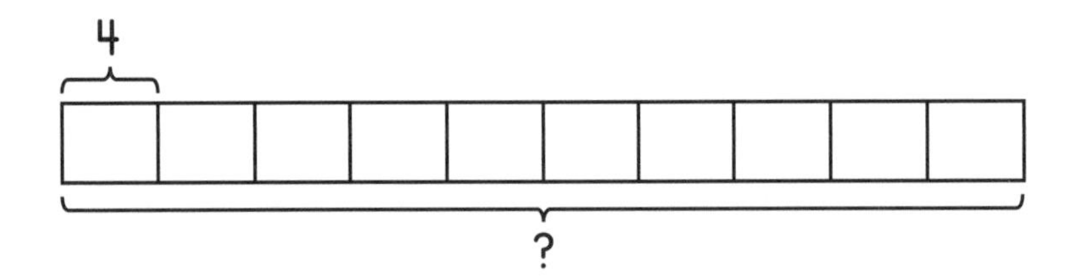


Colleen has ________ pencils in all.

Name: ____________________ Date: ____________

**5.** Alexander buys 8 boxes of erasers.
Each box has 3 erasers.
How many erasers does Alexander have in all?

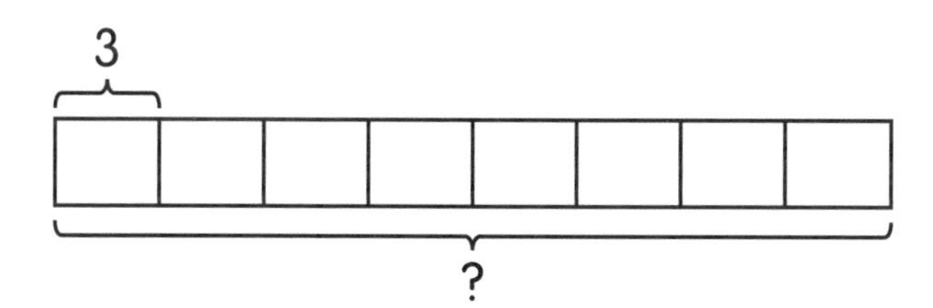


Alexander has ________ erasers in all.

**6.** Neil has 3 crayons.
Each crayon is 10 centimeters long.
He arranges the crayons in a straight line.
What is the total length of the 3 crayons?

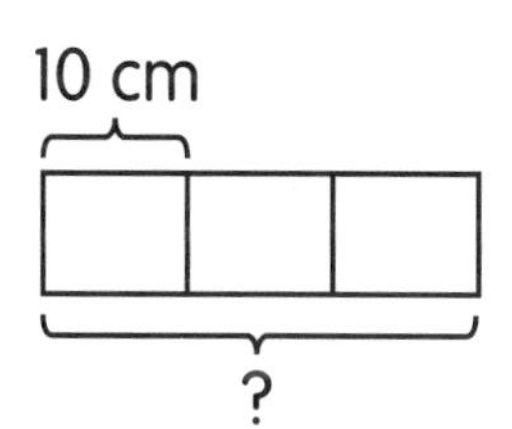


The total length of the 3 crayons is ________ centimeters.

Name: ______________________ Date: ______________

**7.** Ron cuts 6 ribbons so that each ribbon is 10 centimeters long.
What is the total length of the 6 ribbons?

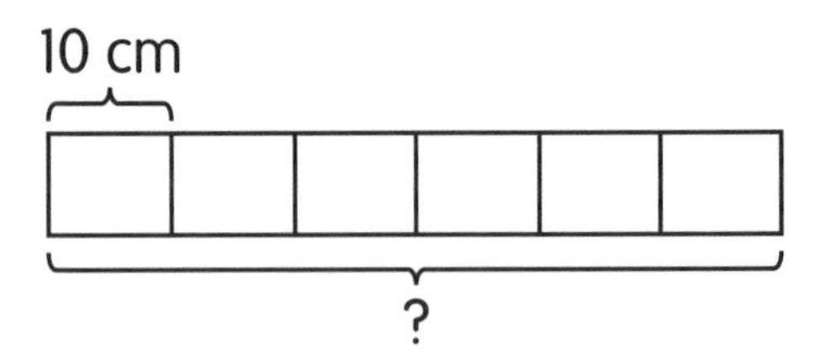


The total length of the 6 ribbons is ________ centimeters.

**8.** Diana puts 8 stickers on each page.
There are 4 pages.
How many stickers does Diana have in all?

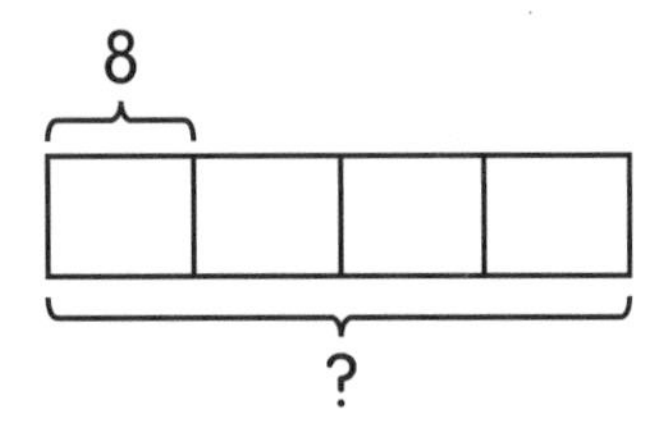


Diana has ________ stickers in all.

Name: ______________________ Date: ______________

# Lesson 2 Real-World Problems: Division

**Solve.**

**Then fill in the blanks.**

**1.** Anita has 18 roses and 3 vases.
She puts an equal number of roses in each vase.
How many roses does she put in each vase?

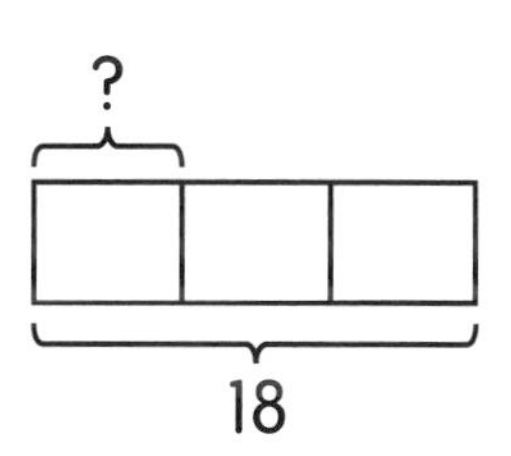


She puts ________ roses in each vase.

**2.** Megan has 16 marbles and 4 cups.
She divides the marbles equally into the cups.
How many marbles are there in each cup?

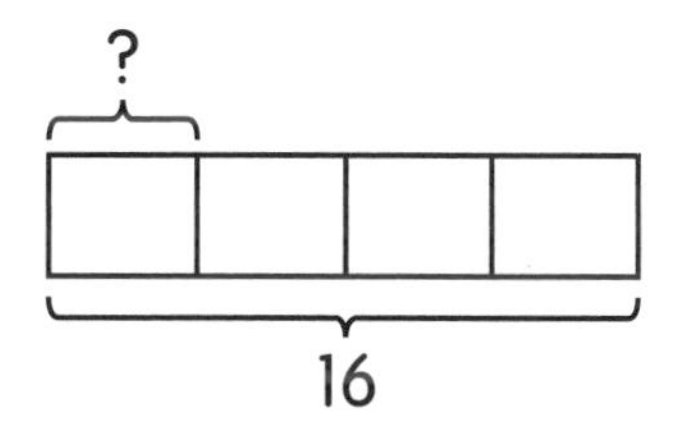


There are ________ marbles in each cup.

Name: ______________________ Date: ______________

**3.** A farmer has some horses in a stable.
There are 20 legs in all.
How many horses are in the stable?

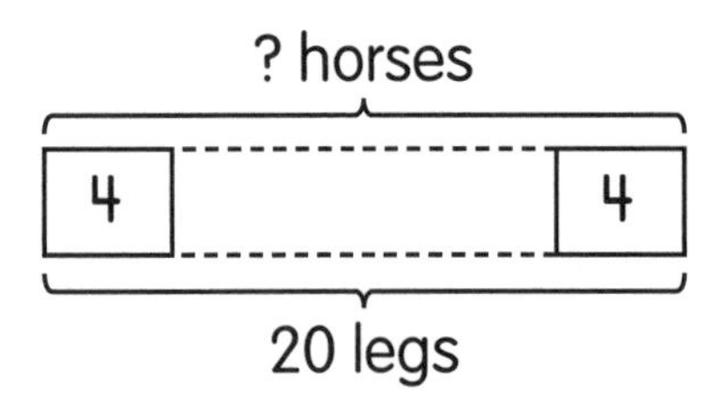


There are ________ horses in the stable.

**4.** Mrs. Lewis bakes 25 snacks for her children.
Each child eats 5 snacks.
How many children does Mrs. Lewis have?

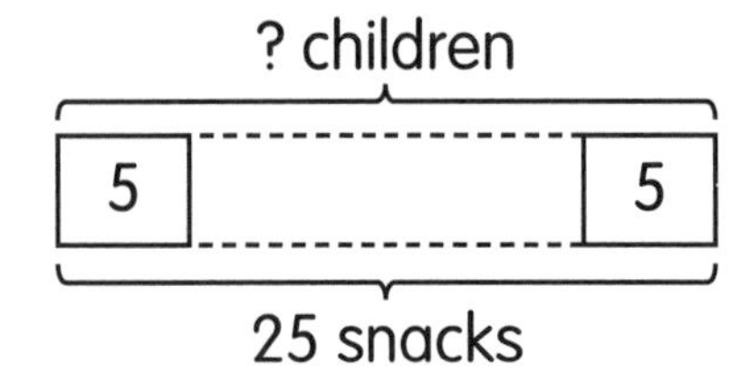


Mrs. Lewis has ________ children.

Name: ______________________ Date: ______________

**Solve.**
**Draw bar models to help you.**

**5.** Joel has 45 baseball cards.
He shares them equally with 5 of his friends.
How many baseball cards does each of them get?

Each of them gets ________ baseball cards.

**6.** Sharon has 15 glasses.
She arranges them equally in 3 rows.
How many glasses are there in each row?

There are ________ glasses in each row.

Name: ______________________ Date: ______________

**7.** A clown has 28 balloons.
He ties 4 balloons into each bunch.
How many bunches of balloons does the clown have?

The clown has ________ bunches of balloons.

**8.** Benjie read 36 pages of a magazine.
He read 4 pages each day.
How many days did it take Benjie to read the magazine?

It took Benjie ________ days to read the magazine.

Name: ______________________ Date: ______________

# Lesson 3 Real-World Problems: Measurement and Money

**State whether you need to multiply or divide.**
**Then solve.**
**Use bar models to help you.**

**1.** Mrs. Wood cuts some lace into 4 pieces.
Each piece of lace is 8 centimeters long.
How long was the lace at first?

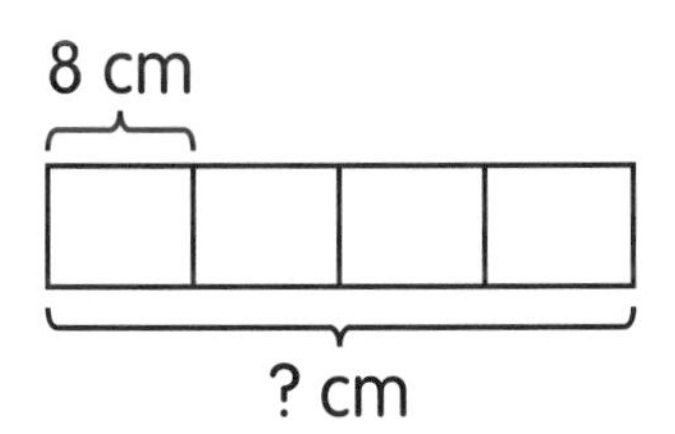


The lace was __________ centimeters long at first.

**2.** Jenna has a piece of cloth that is 30 inches long.
She cuts it into 3 equal pieces.
How long is each piece?

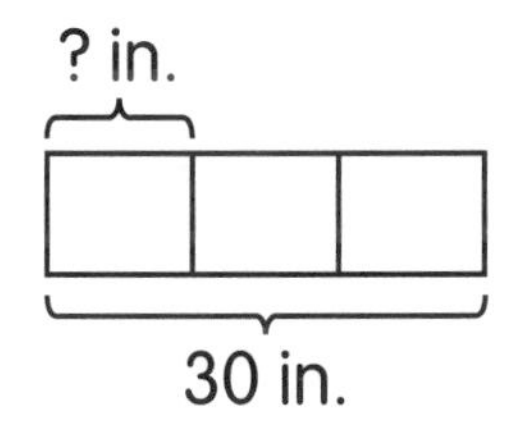


Each piece is __________ inches long.

Name: ______________________ Date: ______________

**State whether you need to multiply or divide.**
**Then solve.**
**Draw bar models to help you.**

**3.** Sarah arranged 7 small boxes end to end in a line.
Each box is 3 inches long.
What is the total length of the boxes?

The total length of the boxes is ________ inches.

**4.** Mina has a rope that is 28 feet long.
She cuts it into equal pieces.
Each piece is 4 feet long.
How many pieces does she cut the rope into?

She cuts the rope into ________ pieces.

Name: ______________________ Date: ______________

**State whether you need to multiply or divide.**
**Then solve.**
**Use bar models to help you.**

**5.** The mass of 5 bags of lemons is 30 kilograms.
Each bag has the same mass.
What is the mass of each bag?

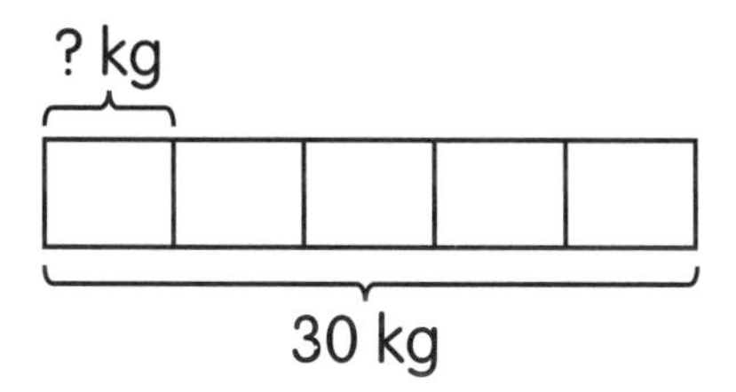


The mass of each bag is ________ kilograms.

**6.** The total mass of some pens is 50 grams.
Each pen has a mass of 5 grams.
How many pens are there?

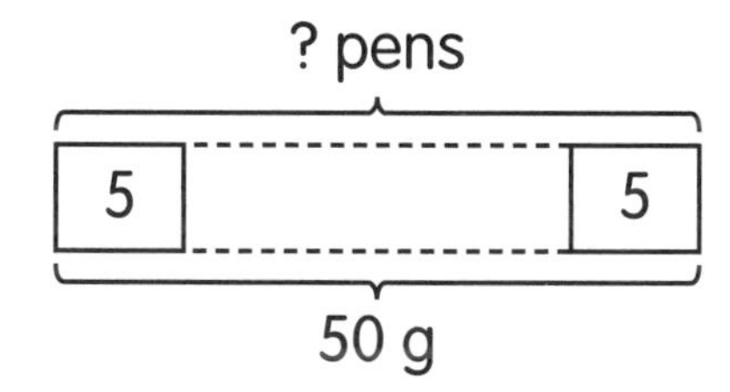


There are ________ pens.

Name: ______________________ Date: ______________

**State whether you need to multiply or divide.**
**Then solve.**
**Draw bar models to help you.**

**7.** Mrs. Willows has 8 crackers.
Each cracker has a mass of 5 grams.
What is the total mass of the 8 crackers?

The total mass of the 8 crackers is ________ grams.

**8.** 27 kilograms of herbs are divided into some bags.
Each bag has a mass of 3 kilograms.
How many bags of herbs are there?

There are ________ bags of herbs.

Name: ______________________ Date: ______________

**State whether you need to multiply or divide.**
**Then solve.**
**Use bar models to help you.**

**9.** Mr. Pierson buys 5 liters of juice every week.
How many liters of juice does Mr. Pierson buy in 5 weeks?

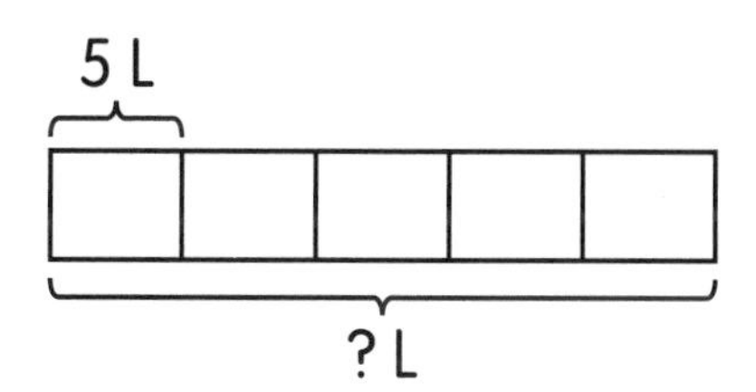


Mr. Pierson buys ________ liters of juice in 5 weeks.

**10.** Abigail pours 35 liters of water into some buckets.
Each bucket has 5 liters of water.
How many buckets are there?

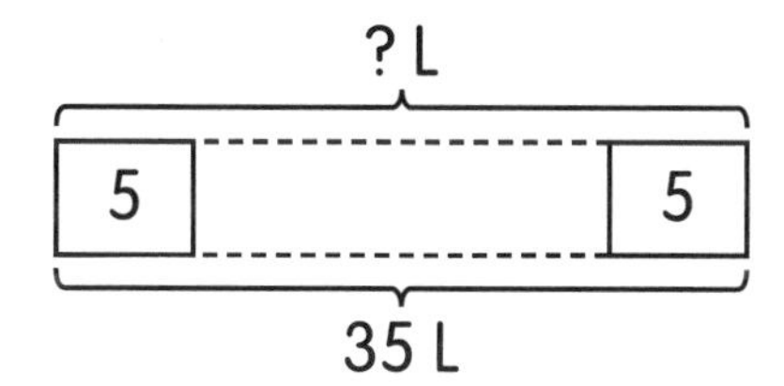


There are ________ buckets.

Name: ______________________ Date: ______________

**State whether you need to multiply or divide.**
**Then solve.**
**Draw bar models to help you.**

**11.** Terell drinks 2 liters of water every day.
How many liters of water does Terell drink in a week?

Terell drinks ________ liters of water in a week.

**12.** Toni pours 16 liters of iced tea equally into 4 jugs.
How much iced tea is there in each jug?

There are ________ liters of iced tea in each jug.

Name: ______________________ Date: ______________

**State whether you need to multiply or divide.**
**Then solve.**
**Use bar models to help you.**

**13.** Mrs. Talley buys 4 boxes of cereal.
Each box of cereal costs $5.
How much does she pay in all?

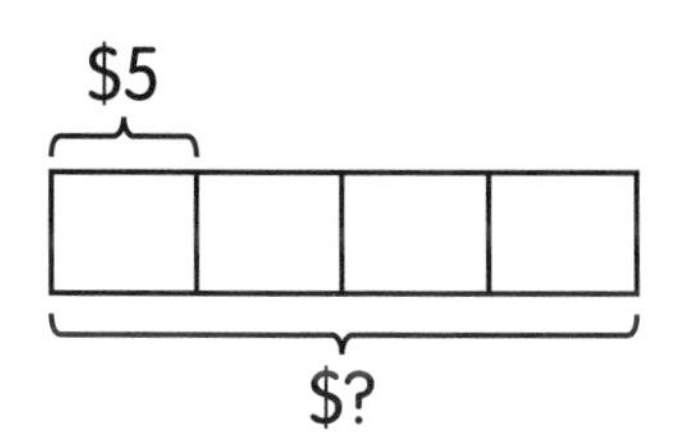


Mrs. Talley pays $________ in all.

**14.** Mr. Kinnear gives $32 to his children.
Each child gets $8.
How many children does Mr. Kinnear have?

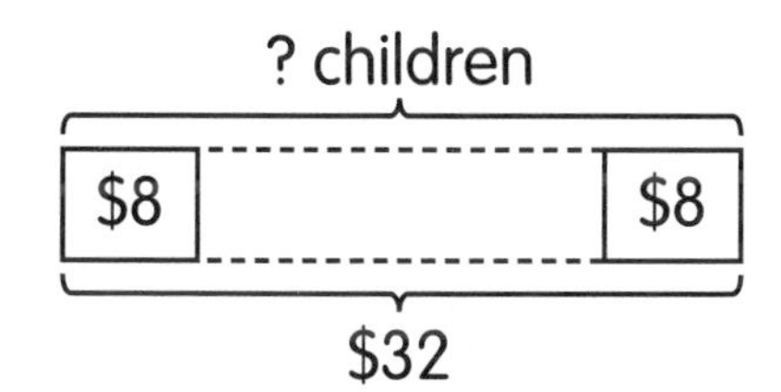


Mr. Kinnear has ________ children.

Name: ______________________ Date: ______________

**State whether you need to multiply or divide.**
**Then solve.**
**Draw bar models to help you.**

**15.** Pauline sells 6 necklaces.
Each necklace costs $10.
How much money does Pauline get?

Pauline gets $________.

**16.** Lauren has $15.
She spends all of it on some books.
Each book costs $5.
How many books does Lauren buy?

Lauren buys ________ books.

Name: ______________________ Date: ______________

1. Amy buys some bags of oranges.
   She puts the oranges into 4 baskets.
   2 baskets of oranges have the same number of oranges as 3 bags.
   How many bags of oranges did Amy buy?

Amy bought __________ bags of oranges.

Name: ______________________ Date: ______________

**2.** Jamie has $40.
She wants to buy some towels.
Each towel costs $8.
How many towels can she buy?

She can buy ________ towels.

Name: ______________________ Date: ______________

# Graphs and Line Plots

## Lesson 1 Reading Picture Graphs with Scales

**Fill in the blanks on page 124. Use the picture graph to help you.**

The picture graph shows the items that Linda bought at a book fair.

**Items Bought at the Book Fair**

| Item | |
|---|---|
| Chapter books | ○○○○○ |
| Binders | ○○○○○○ |
| Coloring books | ○○○○○○ |
| Crayons | ○○○ |
| Comic books | ○○○○ |
| Key: Each ○ stands for 1 item. | |

Name: ______________________ Date: ______________

**Use the picture graph on page 123 to fill in the blanks.**

1. Each ◯ stands for ________.

2. Linda bought ________ comic books.

3. She bought the same number of ________ as coloring books.

4. She bought ________ more chapter books than crayons.

5. She bought ________ items in all.

6. Linda buys two more chapter books the second day.
   How will that change the chart?

   ____________________________________________

   ____________________________________________

   ____________________________________________

Name: ______________________ Date: ______________

The picture graph shows the favorite fruit of students in a class.

**Favorite Fruit of Students in a Class**

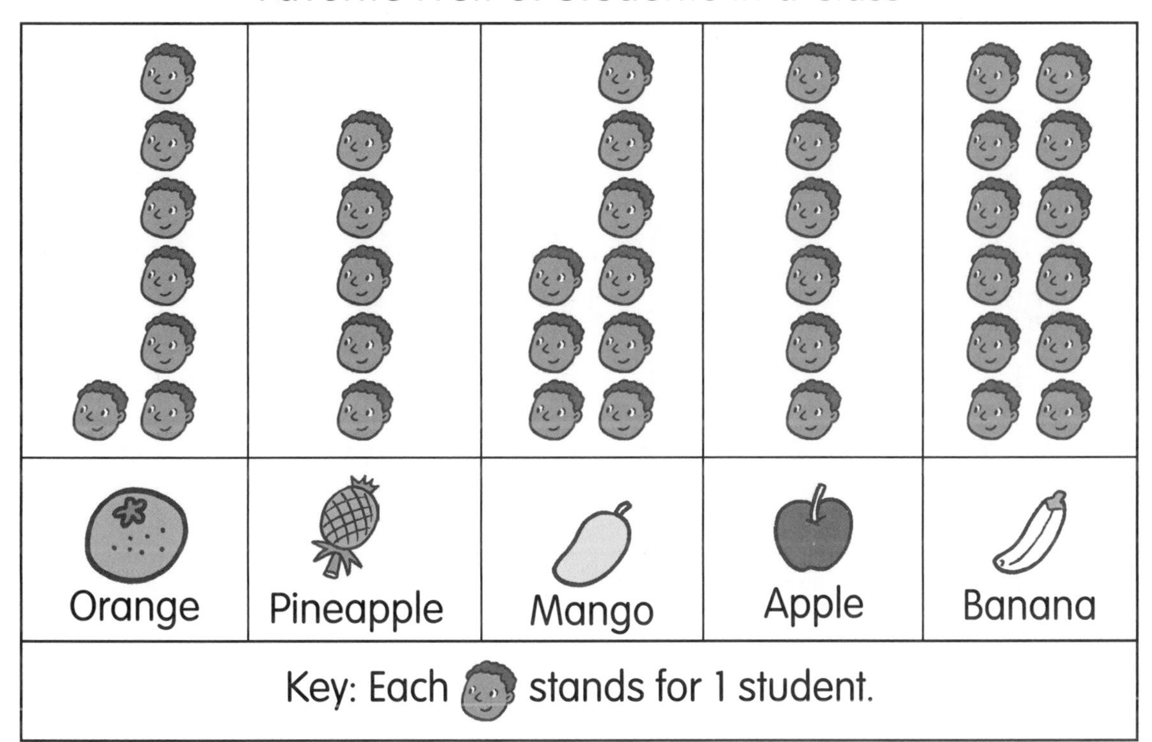


**Use the picture graph to fill in the blanks.**

**7.** __________ students like apples.

**8.** __________ more students like mangoes than pineapples.

**9.** The most favorite fruit is __________.

**10.** There are __________ students in the class.

Name: ______________________ Date: ______________

The picture graph shows the number of stamps 5 children have.

**Number of Stamps 5 Children Have**

| Jackson | Maya | Ben | Reza | Juan |
|---|---|---|---|---|
| Key: Each stamp stands for 5 stamps. | | | | |

**Use the picture graph to fill in the blanks.**

**11.** Juan has __________ stamps.

**12.** __________ has the most stamps.

**13.** __________ has the fewest stamps.

**14.** Ben has __________ stamps more than Jackson.

**15.** Maya has __________ stamps fewer than Reza.

**16.** Maya and Ben have __________ stamps in all.

**17.** After giving __________ stamps to Jackson, Ben will have 20 stamps left.

Name: ______________________ Date: ______________

The picture graph shows the number of children who have read each story.

**Number of Children Who Have Read Each Story**

| *The Cup* | *Jilly and the Pear* | *The Magic Rose* | *Anna Finds a Coin* | *The Doll* |
|---|---|---|---|---|
| ☺☺☺☺ | ☺☺☺☺☺☺ | ☺☺☺☺☺ | ☺☺☺☺☺☺☺☺☺ | ☺☺☺☺☺☺☺ |

Key: Each ☺ stands for 4 children.

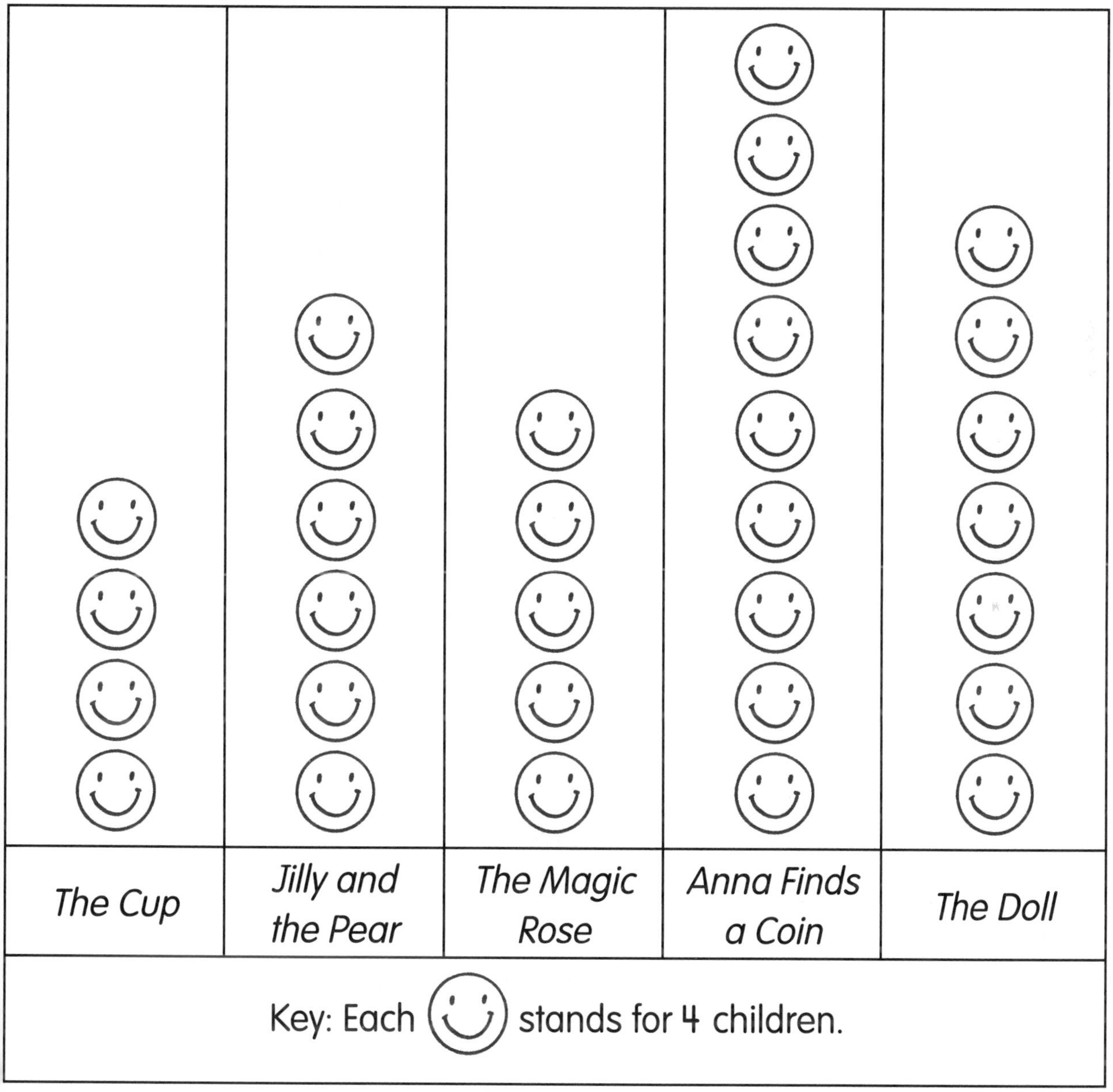

Name: ______________________ Date: ______________

**Use the picture graph on page 127 to answer the questions.**

Use the picture graph on page 127

**18.** Which story is the most popular? ______________

**19.** Which story is the least popular? ______________

**20.** ________ children have read *The Magic Rose.*

**21.** ________ more children have read *The Doll* than *The Cup.*

**22.** The total number of children who have read

*The Cup* and *Jilly and the Pear* is ________.

Name: ______________________ Date: ______________

# Lesson 2 Making Picture Graphs

**1.** Count the items.
Complete the tally chart.

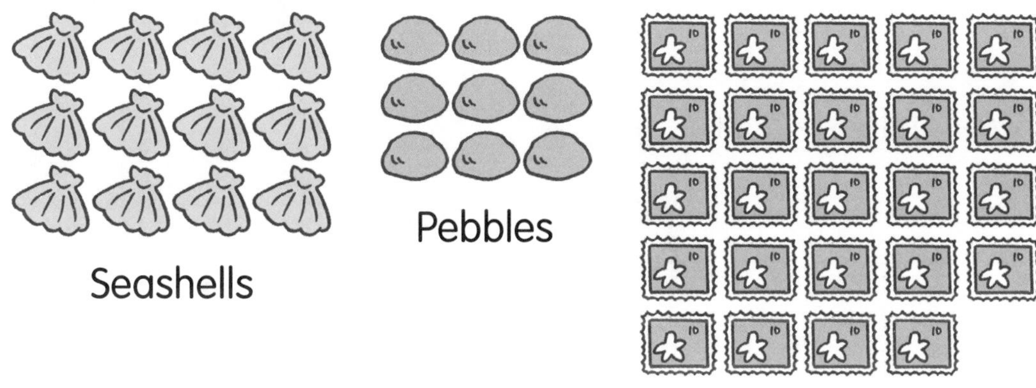

Seashells

Pebbles

Stamps

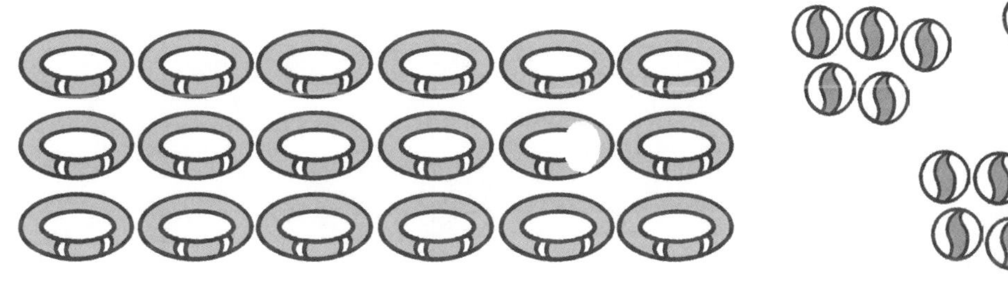

Bracelets

Marbles

| Items | Tally | Number of Items |
|---|---|---|
| Seashells | 𝍸 𝍸 \|\| | 12 |
| Pebbles | | |
| Stamps | | |
| Bracelets | | |
| Marbles | | |

Name: ______________________ Date: ____________

2. Fill in the missing numbers. Use the tally chart on page 129.

| Item | Seashells | Pebbles | Stamps | Bracelets | Marbles |
|---|---|---|---|---|---|
| Number of Items | | | | | |

3. Complete the picture graph.

**Number of Items**

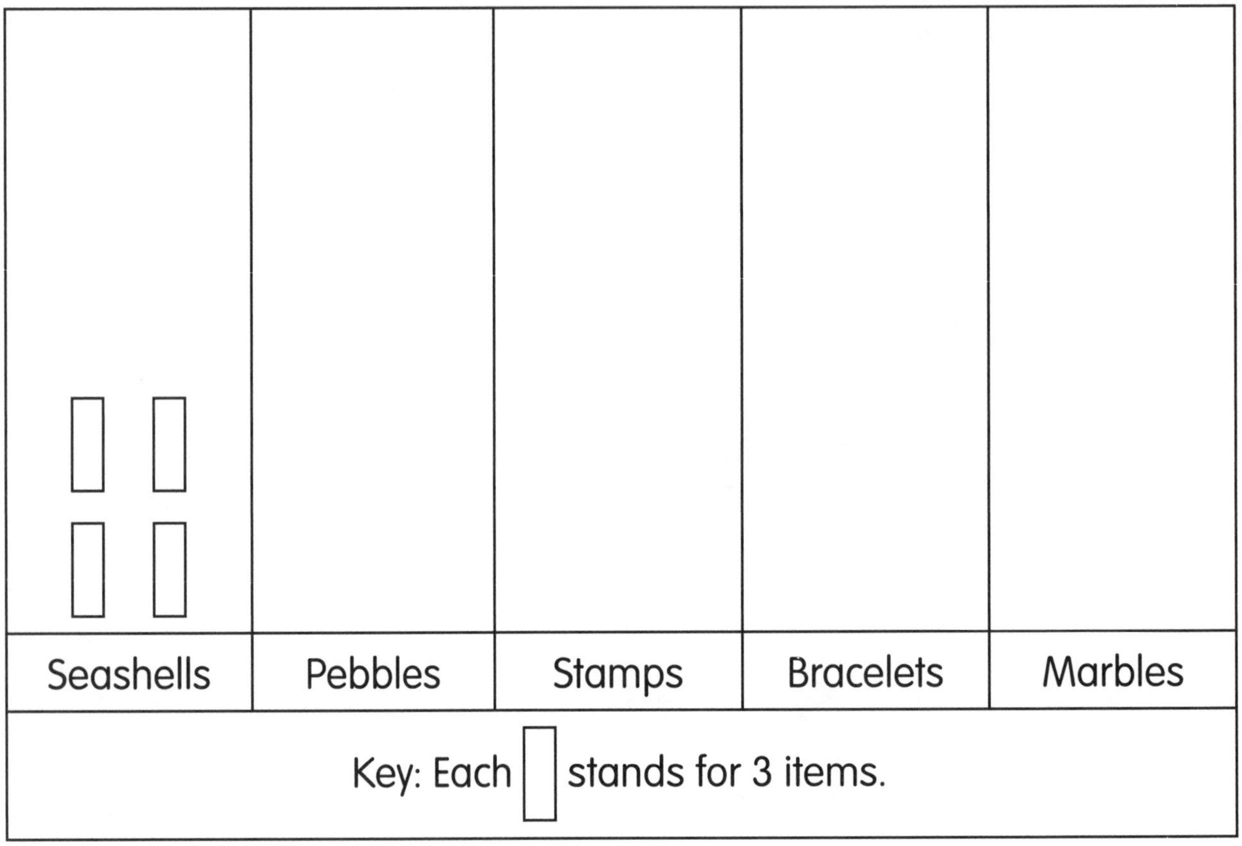

| Seashells | Pebbles | Stamps | Bracelets | Marbles |
|---|---|---|---|---|
| ▯ ▯<br>▯ ▯ | | | | |

Key: Each ▯ stands for 3 items.

**Fill in the blanks.**

4. There are ________ bracelets.

5. There are ________ marbles.

Name: ______________________ Date: ______________

6. **Complete the tally chart.**

A group of children go to a sports complex.
12 children swim.
16 children jog.
8 fewer children play tennis than jog.
The number of children who play badminton is the same as the number of children who swim.
6 more children play squash than badminton.

| Activity | Tally | Number of Children |
|---|---|---|
| Swimming | | |
| Jogging | | |
| Tennis | | |
| Badminton | | |
| Squash | | |

Name: ______________________ Date: ______________

**7.** Use the tally chart on page 131.
Show the number of children by drawing ◯s in the picture graph.

**Activities the Children Do**

| | |
|---|---|
| Swimming | |
| Jogging | |
| Tennis | |
| Badminton | |
| Squash | |
| Key: Each ◯ stands for 2 children. | |

**Fill in the blanks.**

**8.** ________ children go to the sports complex in all.

Name: ______________________ Date: ______________

# Lesson 3 Real-World Problems: Picture Graphs

The picture graph shows the favorite toy of Grade 1 students in a class.

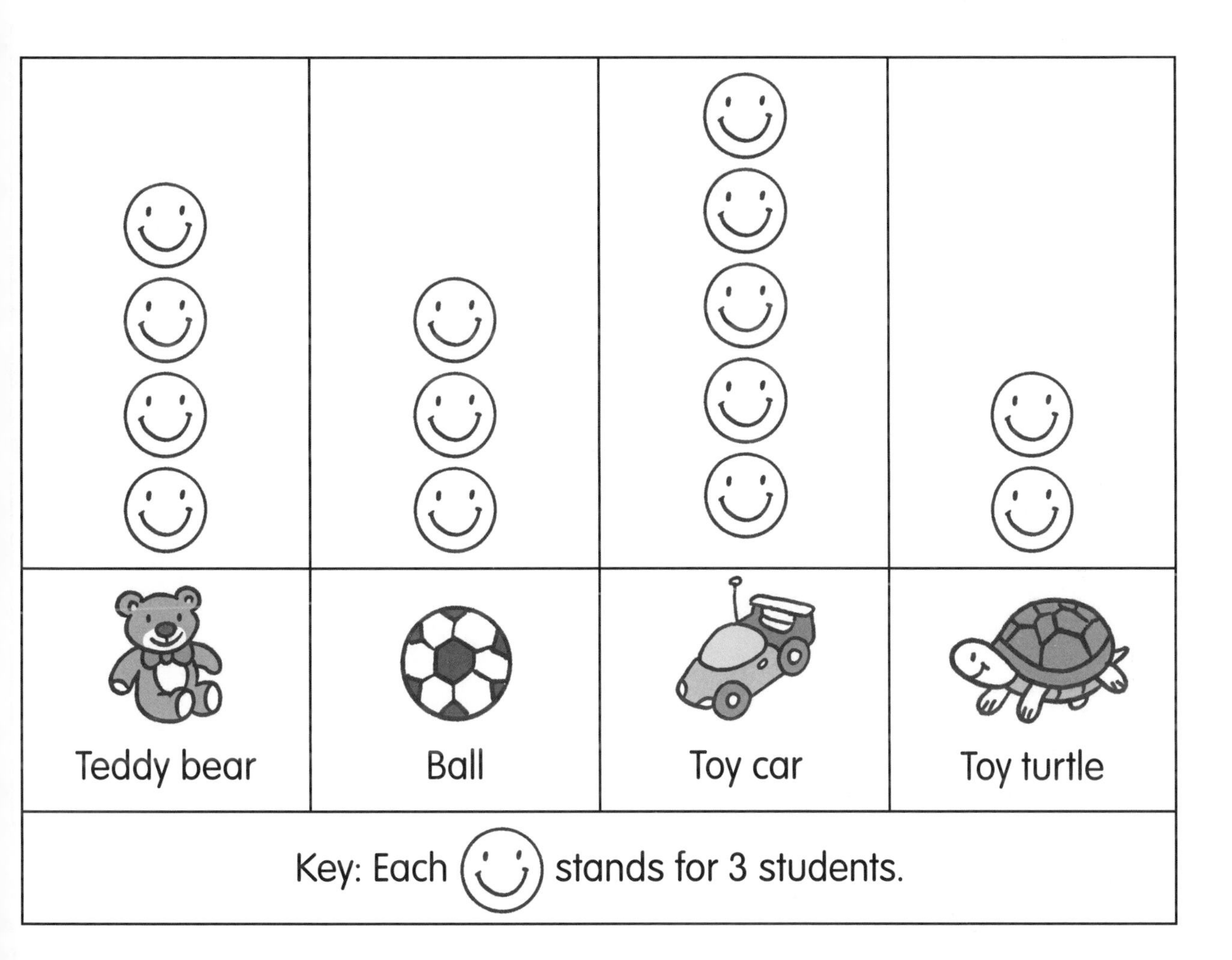


**Use the picture graph to answer the questions.**

**1.** 6 girls like to play with toy cars.
How many boys like to play with toy cars?

______

Name: ______________________ Date: ______________

**2.** 6 boys like to play with balls.
How many girls like to play with balls?

______

**3.** 9 girls like to play with teddy bears.
3 boys like to play with toy turtles.
How many girls like to play with teddy bears and toy turtles in all?

______

**4.** Jenny has some stones in different colors.
Use the data given to finish the picture graph below.
Use a △ to stand for 3 stones.

**a.** There are 9 red stones.
**b.** There are 6 more blue stones than red stones.
**c.** There are 9 more yellow stones than blue stones.
**d.** There are 3 fewer green stones than yellow stones.
**e.** There is the same number of purple stones as blue stones.

Title: ______________________

| | | | | |
|---|---|---|---|---|
| | | | | |
| Red | Blue | Yellow | Green | Purple |
| Key: Each ______ stands for 3 stones. | | | | |

Name: ______________________ Date: ______________

# Lesson 4 Bar Graphs and Line Plots

**1.** Count the number of letters in each name.
Then complete the table.

| Name | Number of Letters | Name | Number of Letters |
|---|---|---|---|
| Jessica | | Barry | |
| Brenda | | Zoe | |
| Carl | | Ann | |
| Fiona | | Nicole | |

**Use the data in the table to complete the bar graph.**

**2.**

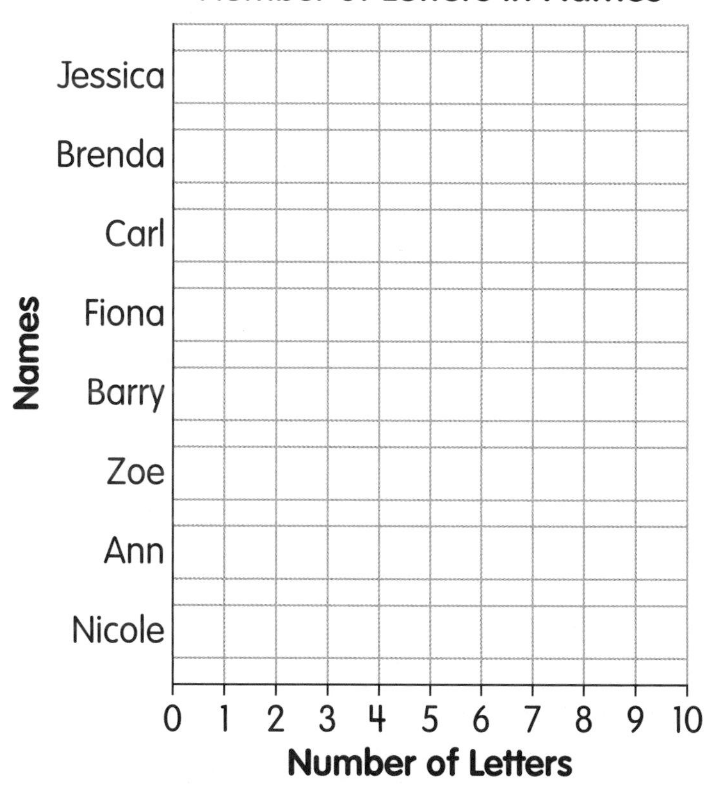

Name: ______________________ Date: ______________

**Use the data in the bar graph on page 135 to complete the line plot.**

**3.**

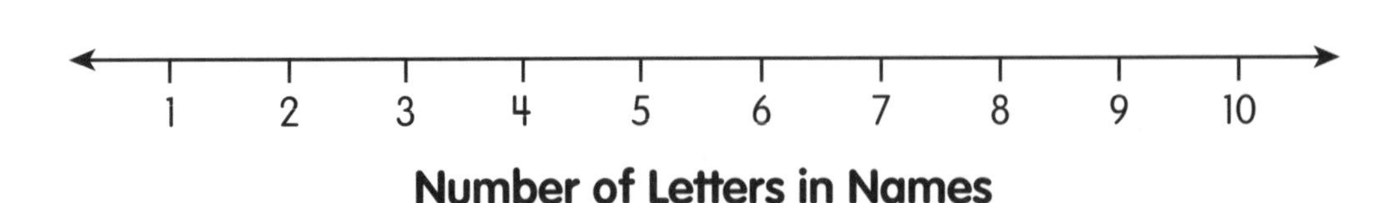


**Use the data in the line plot below to fill in the blanks.**

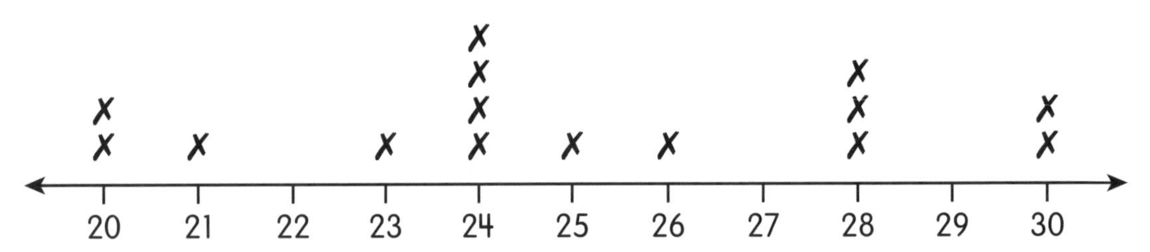


**4.** ________ students took the test.

**5.** Most students scored ________ points.

**6.** ________ students scored less than 24 points.

**7.** ________ students scored the highest points.

Name: ______________________________ Date: ____________________

The table shows the length of some children's feet in centimeters.

| Length (cm) | 14 | 16 | 18 | 20 | 22 |
| --- | --- | --- | --- | --- | --- |
| Number of children | 3 | 5 | 2 | 4 | 1 |

**Draw a line plot to show the data from the chart. Then fill in the blanks.**

**8.**

**Length of Children's Feet (cm)**

**9.** __________ children's feet were measured .

**10.** Most children have feet that are __________ centimeters long.

**11.** The shortest length of the children's feet is __________ centimeters.

**12.** __________ children have feet more than 18 centimeters.

Name: ______________________ Date: ______________

The line plot shows the number of mistakes in a math exercise made by students in a class.

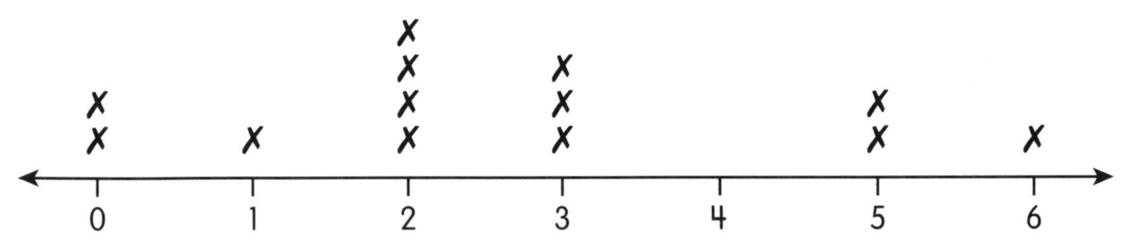


**Fill in the blanks.**

**13.** __________ students are in the class.

**14.** __________ students did not make any mistakes.

**15.** Most students made __________ mistakes.

**16.** __________ students made more than 4 mistakes.

Name: ______________________ Date: ______________

# Put on Your Thinking Cap!

Andy arranges his coins, stamps, stickers, and postcards in different albums.

| Number of each type of item | Description of album used |
|---|---|
| 8 coins | Has stars and a smiley face |
| 12 stamps | Has no sun |
| 6 stickers | Has the most triangles |
| 14 postcards | Has a sun |

Album 2

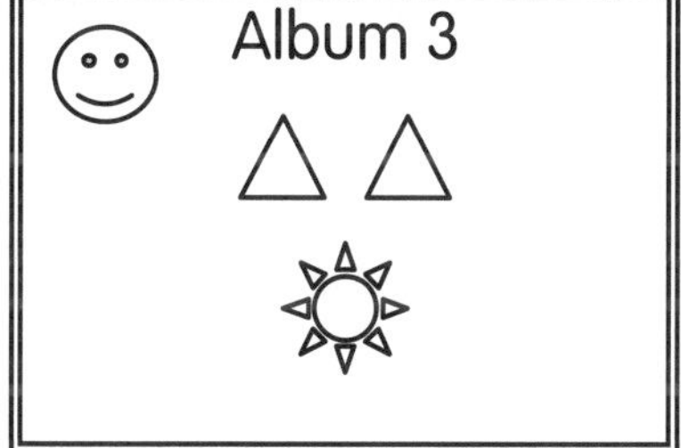


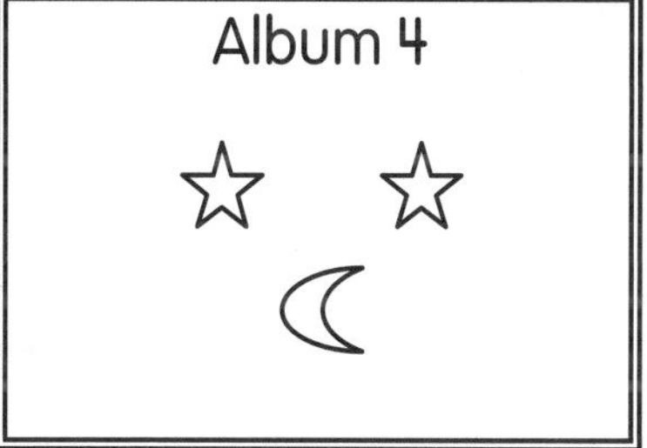

Name: ______________________ Date: ______________

**Use the given data on page 139 to complete the picture graph. Use ☒ to stand for 2 items.**

**1.** **Items in Different Albums**

| | | | |
|---|---|---|---|
| | | | |
| Coin | Stamp | Sticker | Postcard |
| Key: Each ☒ stands for 2 items. | | | |

**Fill in the blanks.**

**2.** Album __________ contains coins.

**3.** Album __________ contains stamps.

**4.** Album __________ contains stickers.

**5.** Album __________ contains postcards.

Name: ______________________ Date: ______________

# Lines and Surfaces

## Lesson 1 Parts of Lines and Curves

**Fill in the blanks.**

How many parts of lines and curves does each figure have?

**1.**

The figure has ________ parts of lines and ________ curves.

**2.**

The figure has ________ parts of lines and ________ curves.

**3.**

The figure has ________ parts of lines and ________ curves.

Name: ______________________ Date: ______________

**Look at these numbers and letters.**

8 4 5 3 b e

Which of these have

4. parts of lines only? ________

5. curves only? ________

6. parts of lines and curves? ________

Draw a letter using a part of line and a curve.

7.

**Color the figures that have a part of a line and a curve.**

8.

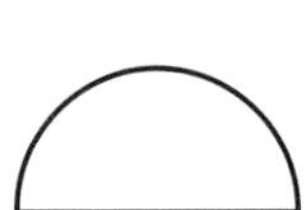

Name: ______________________ Date: ______________

**Joanna draws some pictures with parts of lines and curves. Count the parts of lines and curves she used.**

**9.**

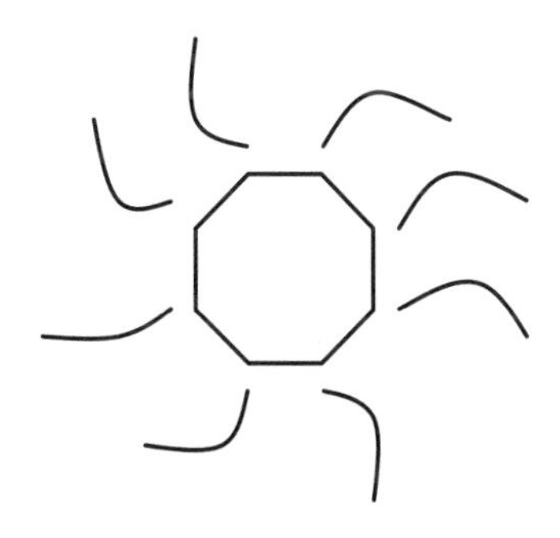

_______ parts of lines and _______ curves.

**10.**

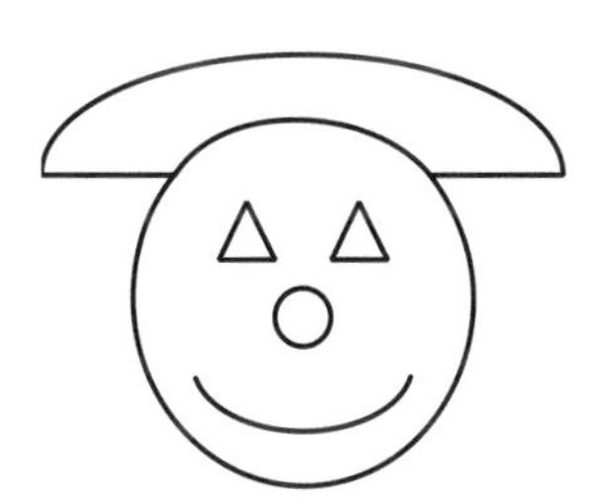

_______ parts of lines and _______ curves.

**11.**

_______ parts of lines and _______ curves.

Name: ______________________ Date: ______________

**Draw a picture with**

**12.** more than 3 parts of lines.

**13.** fewer than 9 curves.

**14.** more than 12 parts of lines and curves.

Name: ______________________ Date: ______________

# Lesson 2 Flat and Curved Surfaces

**Look at the objects.**
**Then fill in the blanks.**

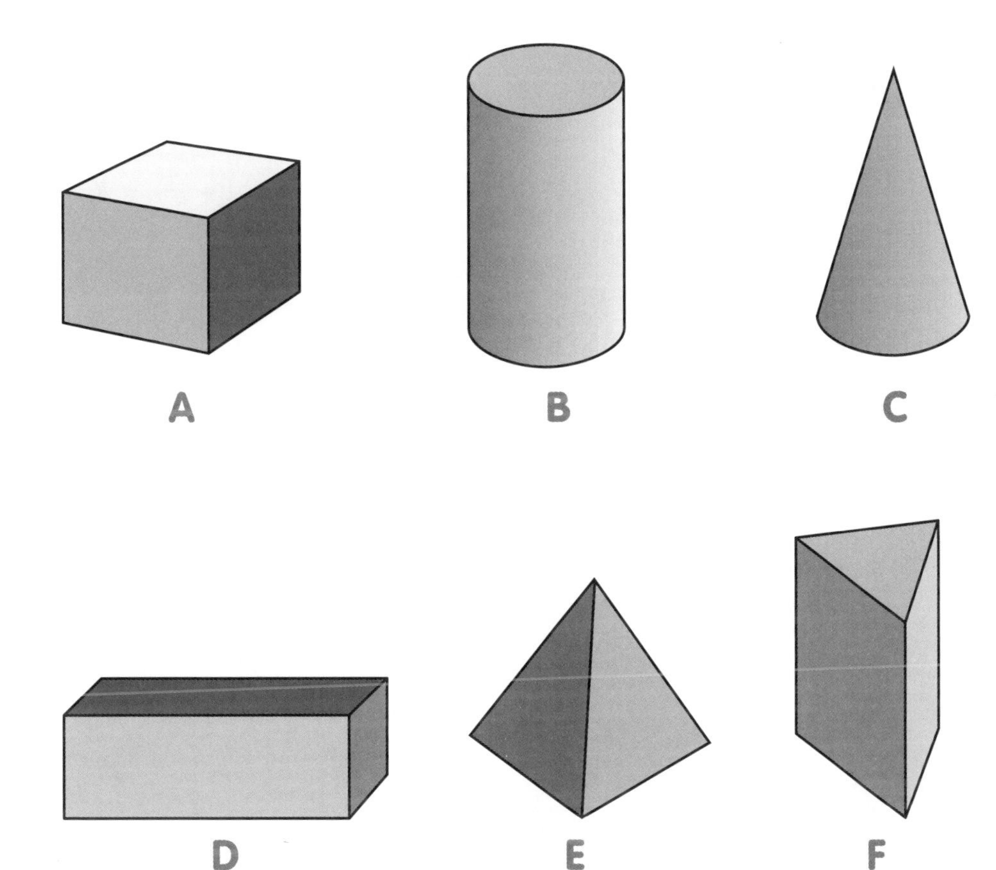


1.

| Object | Number of flat surfaces | Number of curved surfaces |
|---|---|---|
| A | | |
| B | | |
| C | | |
| D | | |
| E | | |
| F | | |

Name: ____________________ Date: ____________

**Look at the objects.**
**Then fill in the blanks.**

**2.**

The can has ________ flat surfaces

and ________ curved surface.

**3.**

The hat has ________ curved surface.

**4.**

The tissue box has ________ flat surfaces.

Name: ____________________ Date: ____________

Circle the solids that you can stack.

5.

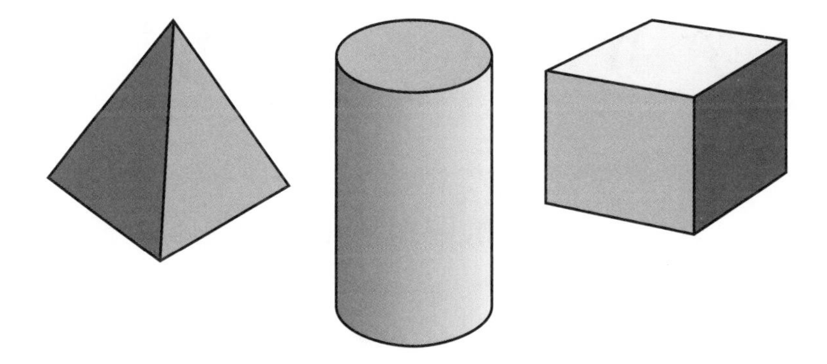

Circle the solids that you can roll.

6.

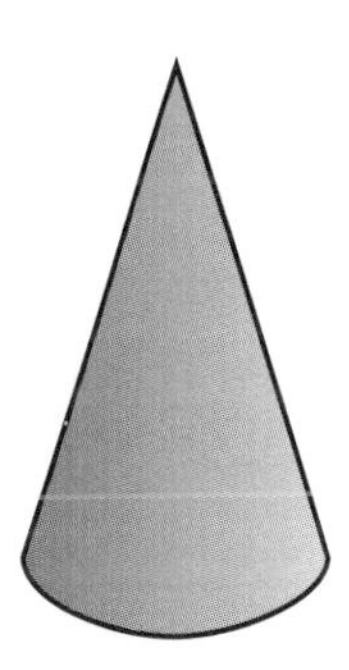

Circle the solids that you can slide.

7.

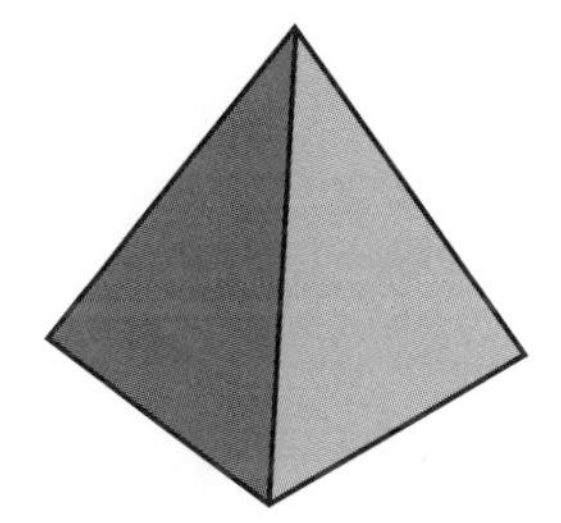

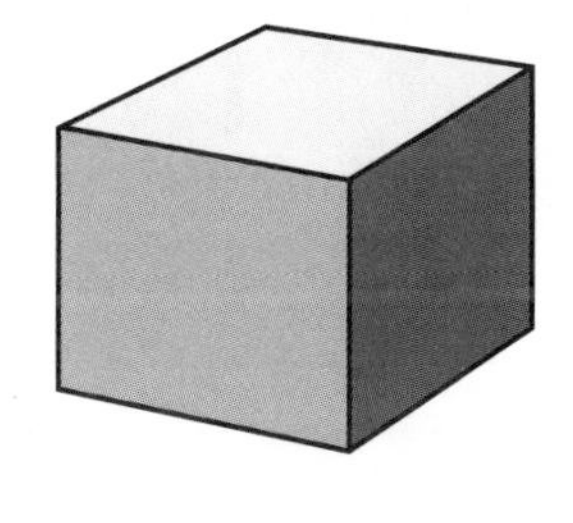

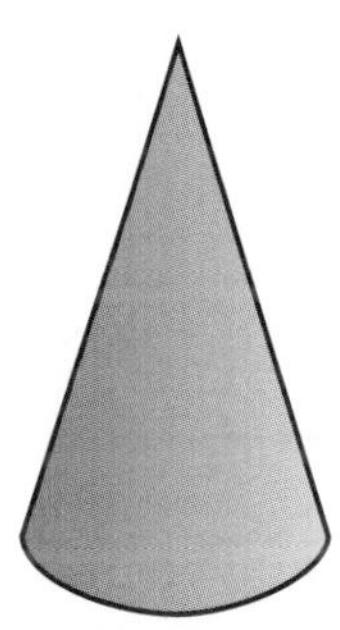

Name: ______________________ Date: ______________

# Put on Your Thinking Cap!

1. Here are some shapes.
   Use the dotted lines to help you draw these shapes.

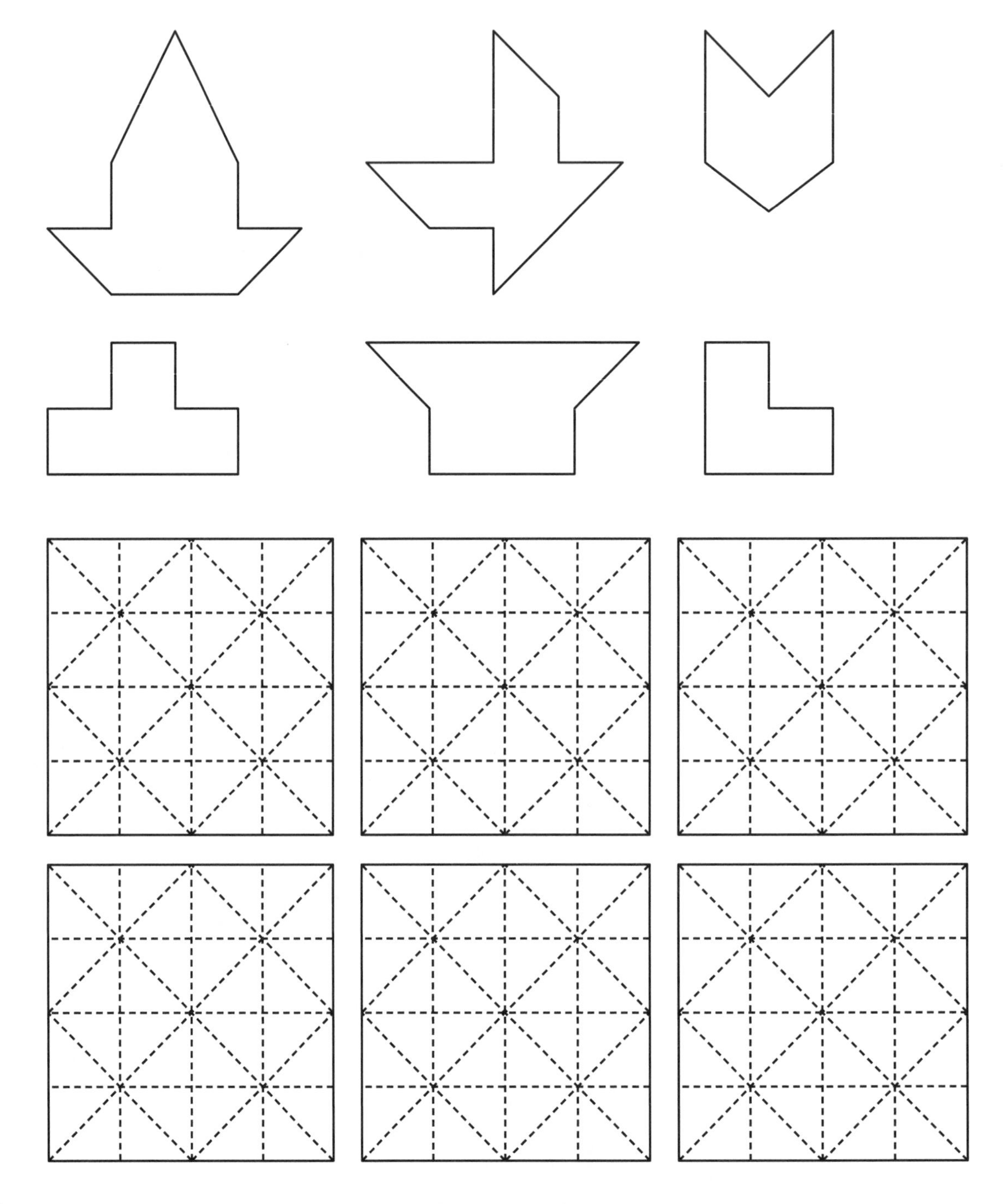

Name: ______________________ Date: ______________

# Shapes and Patterns

## Lesson 1 Plane Shapes

**Look at the shapes.**

**1.** Color the hexagons red, the circles blue, the triangles yellow, the rectangles green, and the trapezoids purple.

Name: ______________________ Date: ______________

**Draw lines on each shape to show the smaller shapes: triangles or squares.**

**2.**

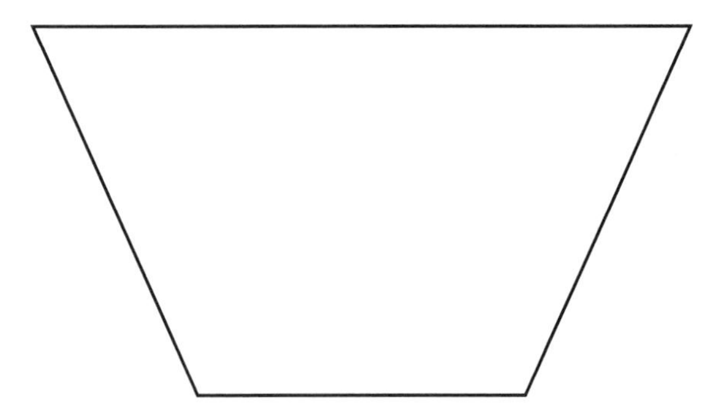

**3.**

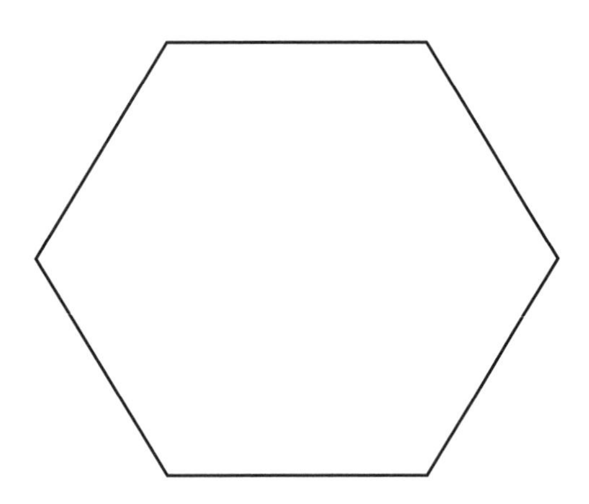

**4.**

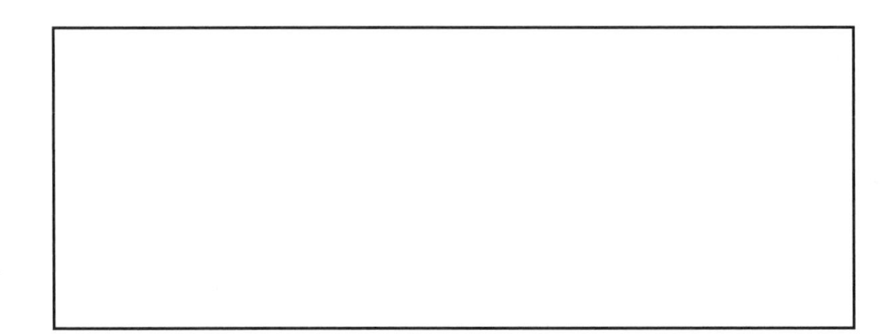

Name: ______________________ Date: ______________

**5.** Draw lines on each figure to show how it is made with these shapes: triangle, square, rectangle, trapezoid, and hexagon.

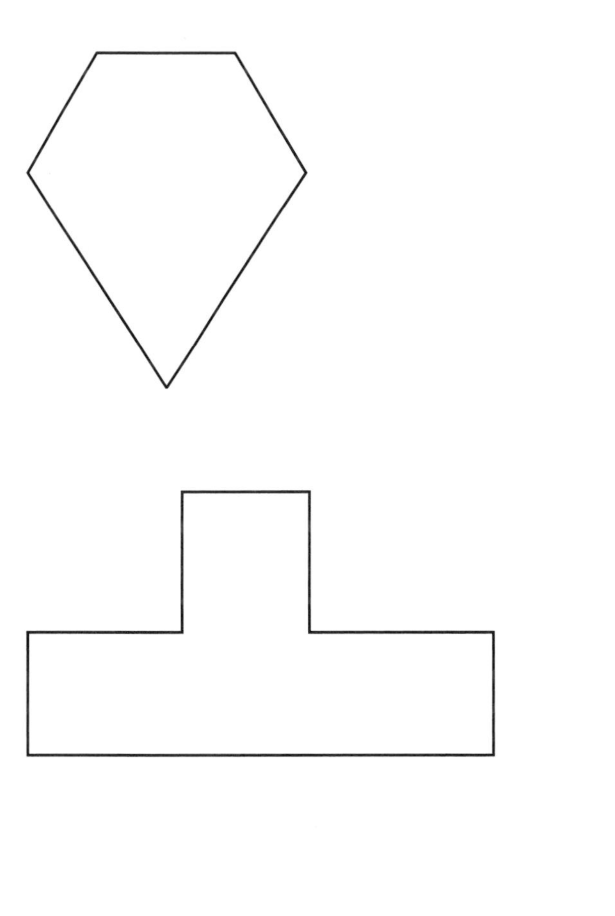

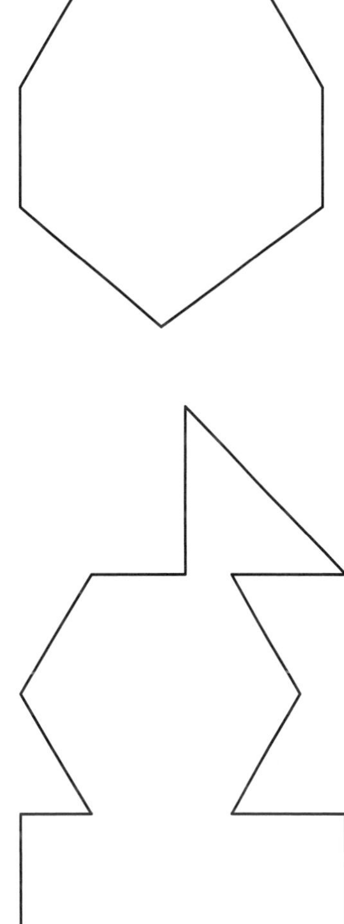

Name: ______________________________ Date: ________________

**Each figure is made with two shapes.**
**Name the shapes.**

**6.**

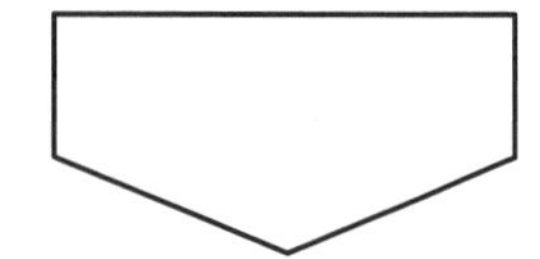

The figure is made with a ________ and a ________.

**7.**

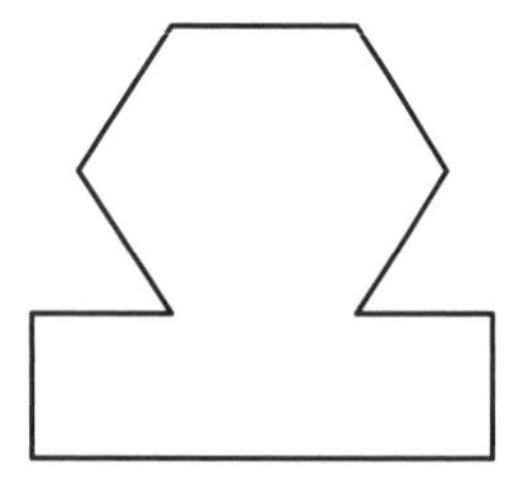

The figure is made with a ________ and a ________.

**8.**

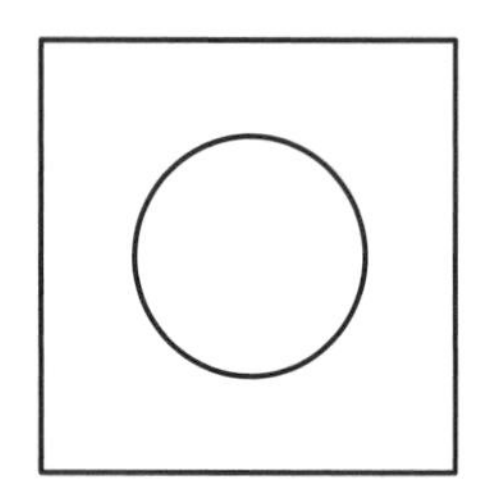

The figure is made with a ________ and a ________.

**9.**

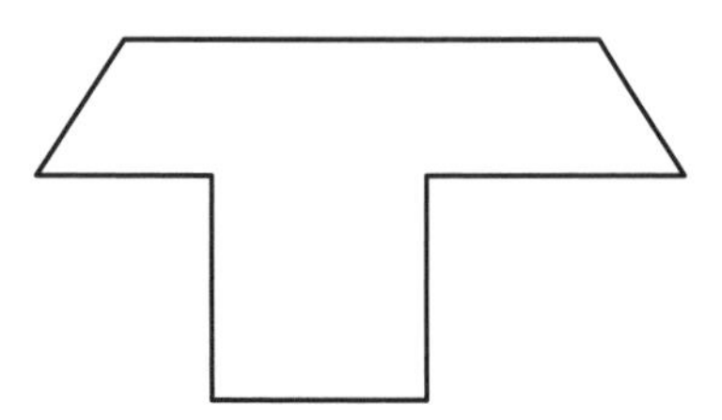

The figure is made with a ________ and a ________.

Name: ______________________ Date: ______________

## Copy each figure.

**10.**

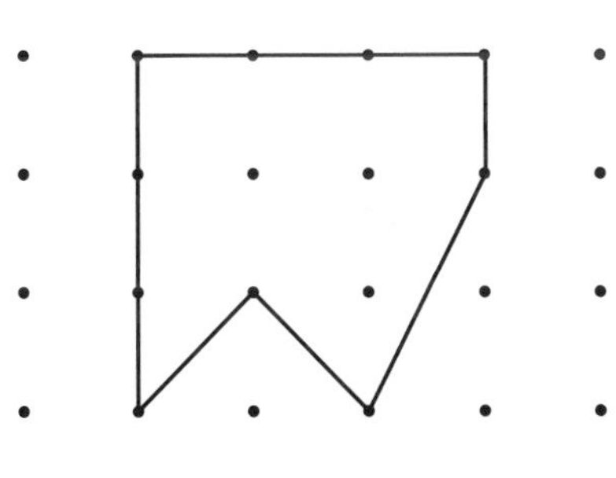

**11.**

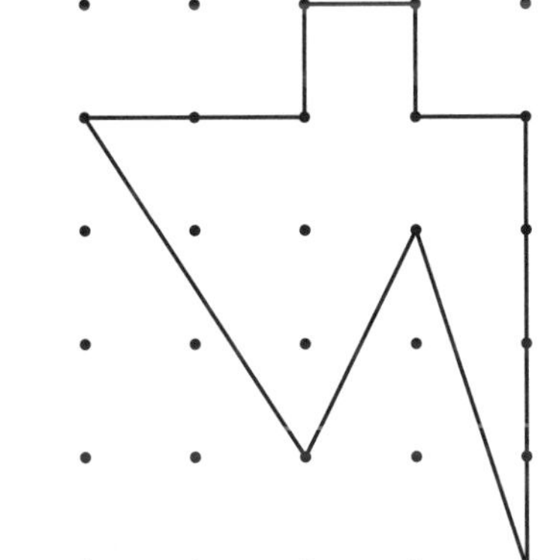

**12.**

Name: ______________________ Date: ______________

## Copy each figure.

**13.**

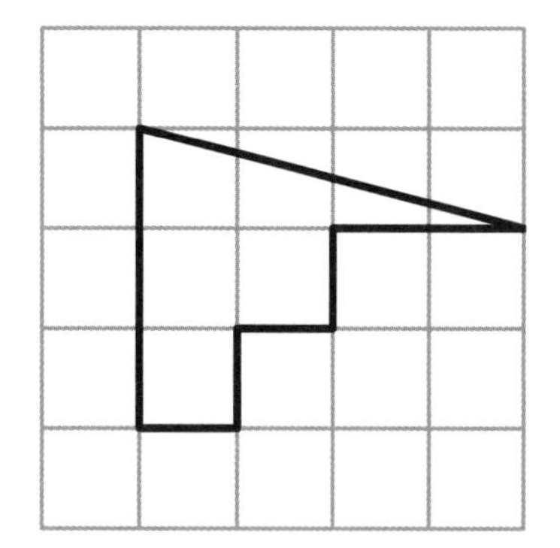

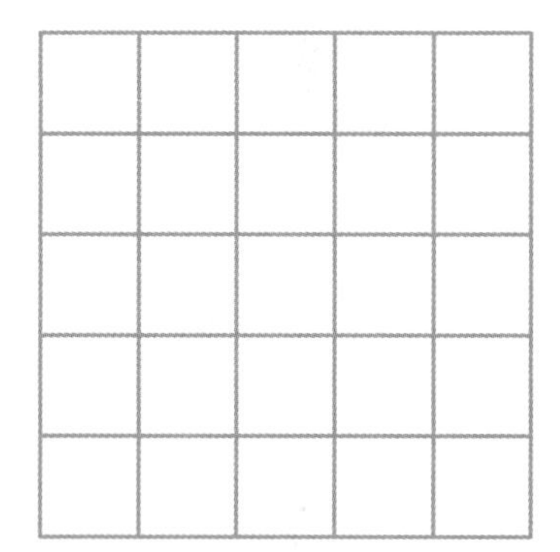

**14.**

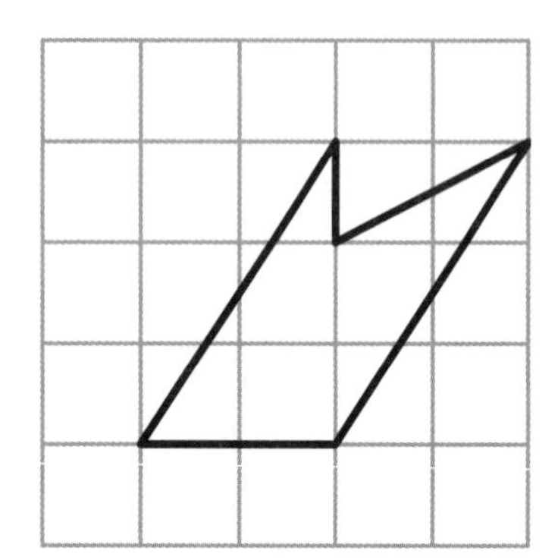

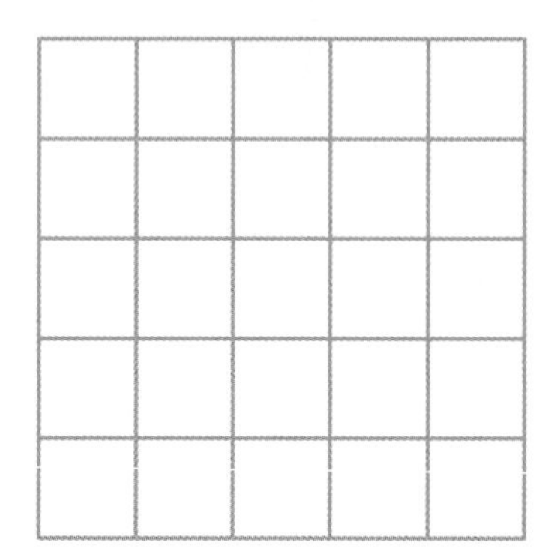

**15.**

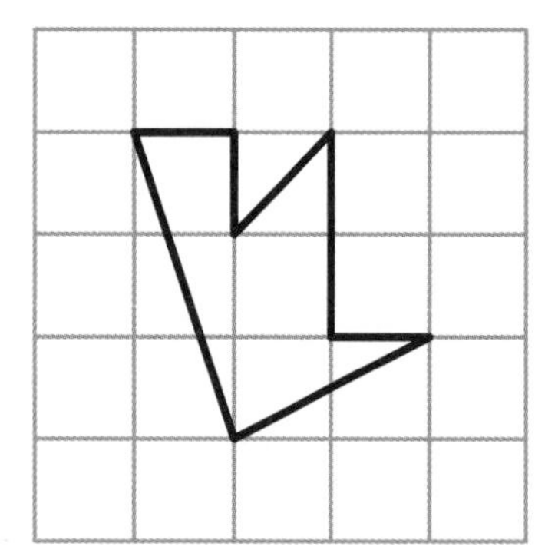

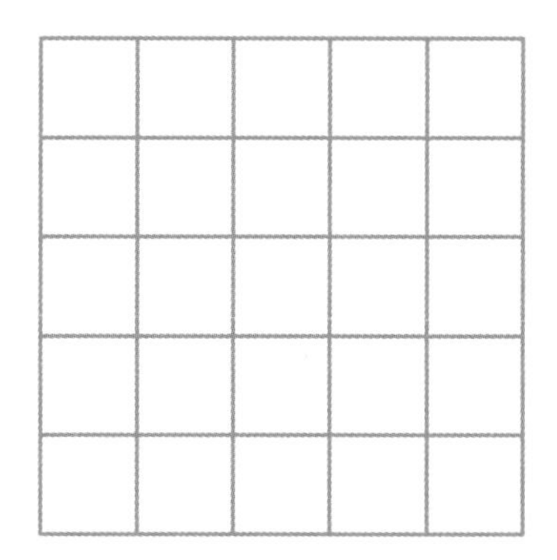

**16.**

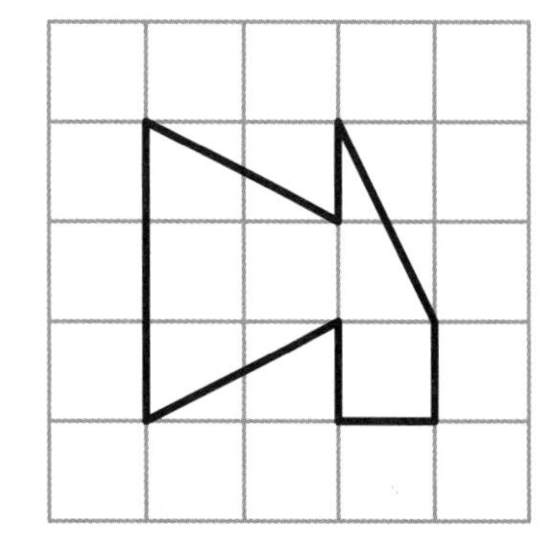

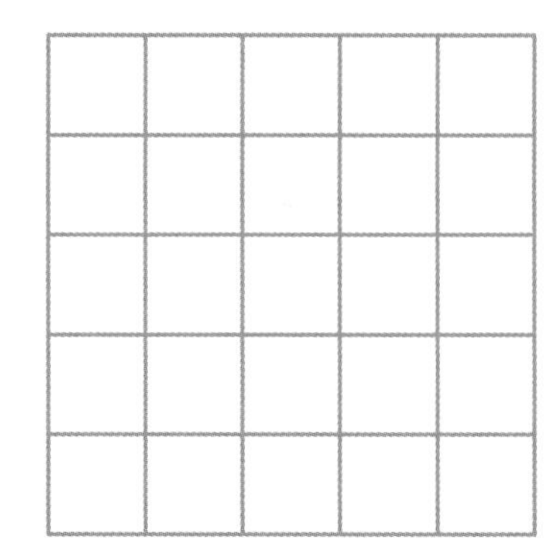

Name: ______________________ Date: ______________

**17.** Match each shape with its name.

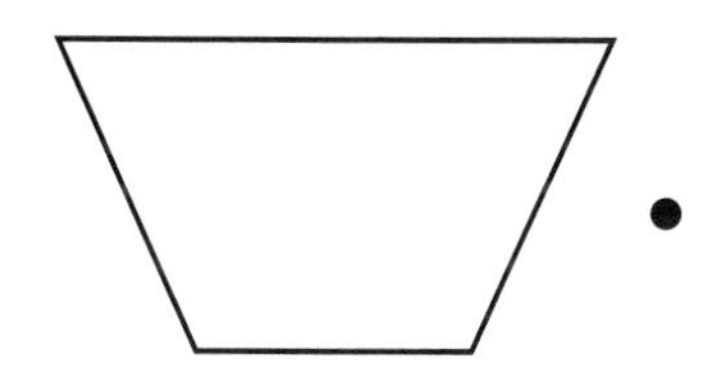 • • hexagon

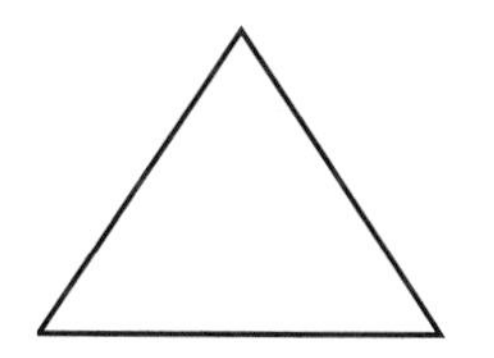 • • trapezoid

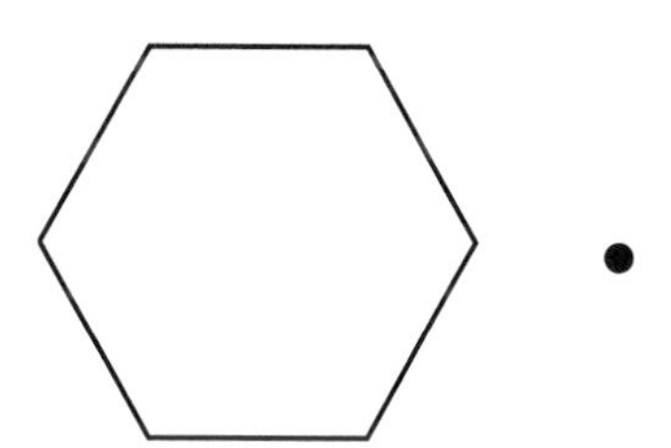 • • pentagon

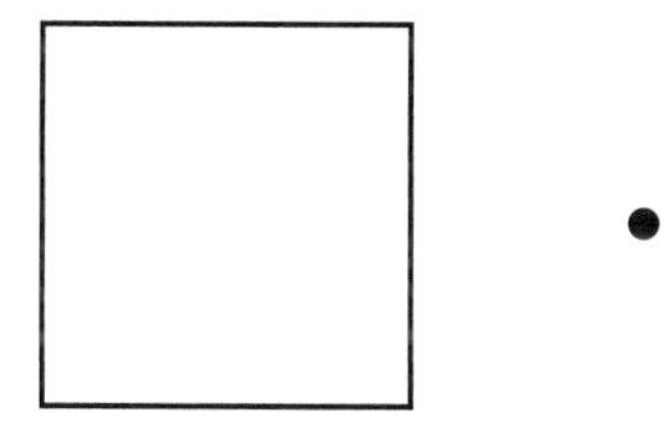 • • triangle

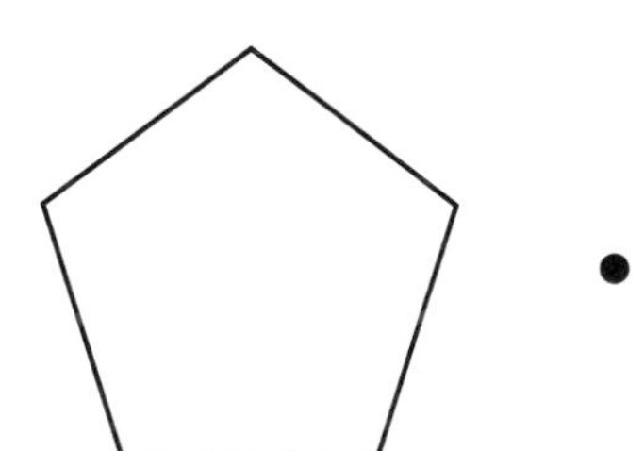 • • square

Name: ________________________ Date: ________________

**Read.**
**Then fill in each blank with the correct shape in the box.**

| hexagon | quadrilateral | pentagon |
|---|---|---|
| square | rectangle | triangle |

**18.** I have 3 sides and 3 angles.

I am a ________________.

**19.** I have 4 sides and 4 angles.

I am a ________________.

**20.** I have 4 equal sides and 4 angles.

I am a ________________.

**21.** I have 5 sides and 5 angles.

I am a ________________.

**22.** I have 6 sides and 6 angles.

I am a ________________.

**23.** I have 4 sides and 4 angles. My opposite sides are equal.

I am a ________________.

Name: ______________________ Date: ______________

# Lesson 2 Solid Shapes

**Write the number of solid shapes used in each model.**

1.

| Solid Shape | Number |
|---|---|
| cube | |
| cylinder | |
| rectangular prism | |
| sphere | |

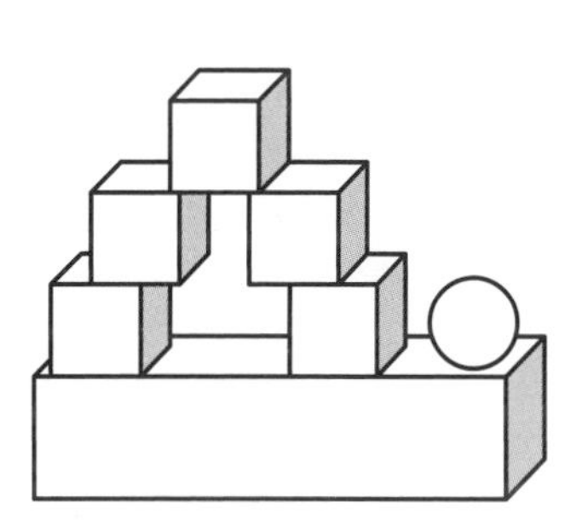

2.

| Solid Shape | Number |
|---|---|
| cube | |
| cylinder | |
| cone | |
| pyramid | |

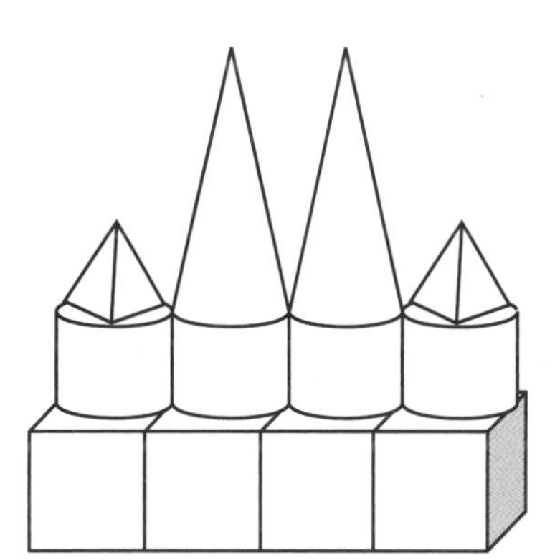

Name: ______________________ Date: ______________

**Write the number of solid shapes used in the model.**

**3.**

| Solid Shape | Number |
|---|---|
| Rectangular prism | |
| Cube | |
| Cone | |
| Cylinder | |
| Sphere | |

**4. Draw lines on the cube to show how it is made of six faces.**

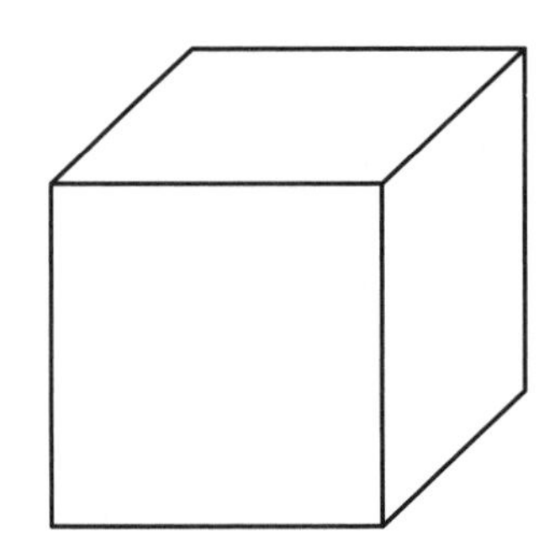

Name: ______________________ Date: ______________

# Lesson 3 Making Patterns

**Look at the pattern.**
**Draw what comes next.**

1. 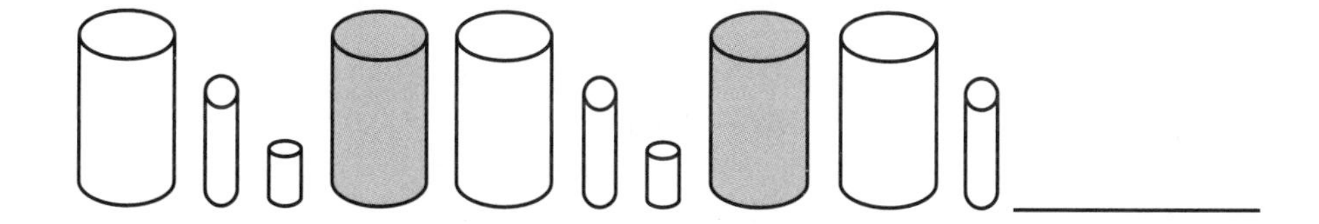

2. 

3. 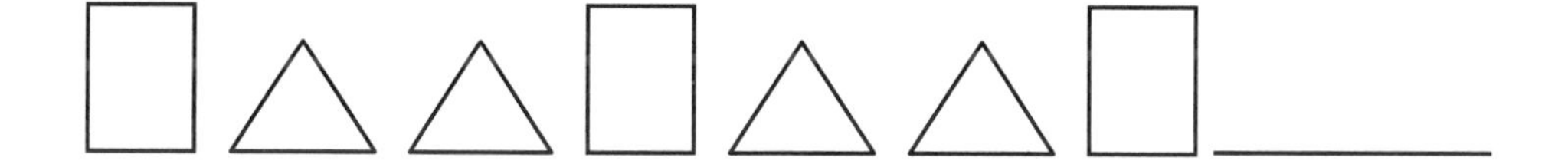

Name: ______________________ Date: ______________________

**Circle the correct shapes or figures made of shapes to complete the pattern.**

**4.**

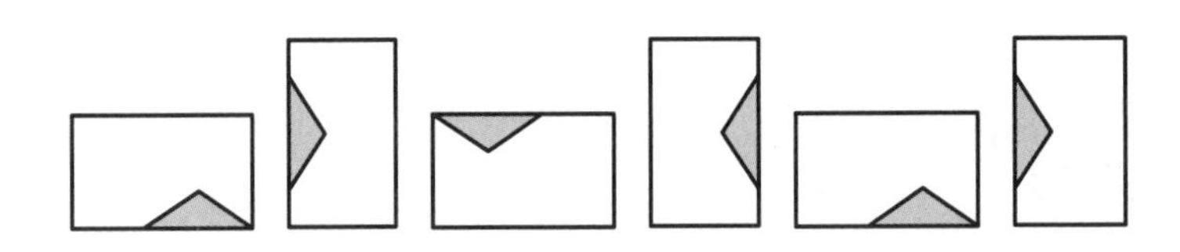

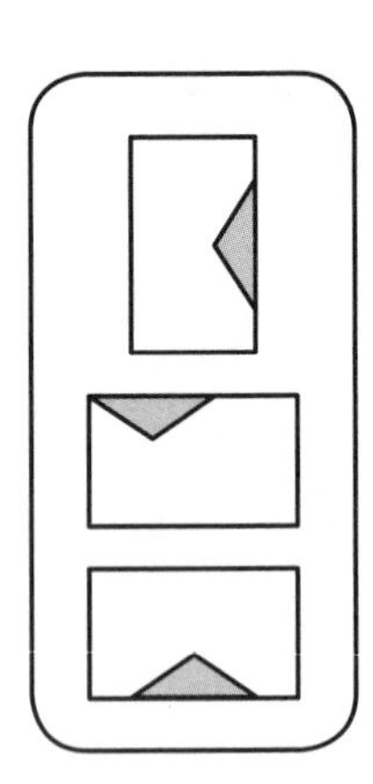

**5.**

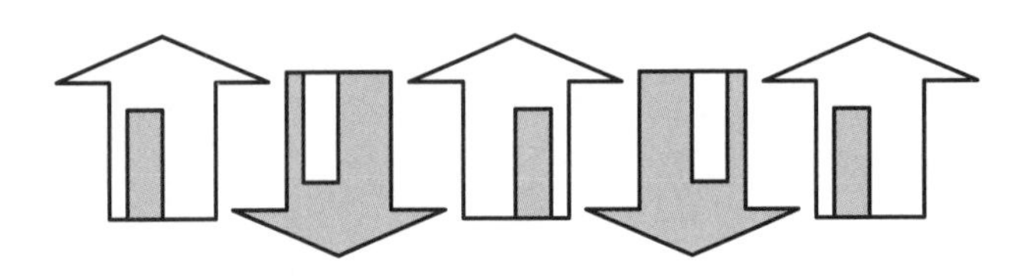

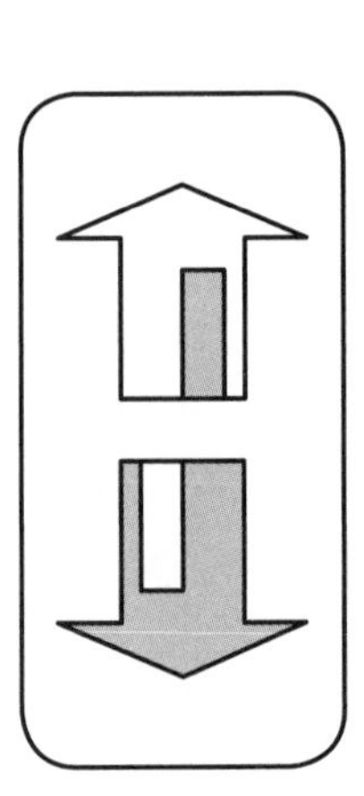

Name: ______________________ Date: ______________

# Put on Your Thinking Cap!

**Copy each group of shapes.**
**Then cut out the shapes.**
**Try to form a rectangle from each group of shapes.**
**Which group(s) of shapes can form a rectangle?**

**Here are two simple rules to follow.**

**a.** **All cut-outs must be used.**

**b.** **Cut-outs cannot overlap.**

**1.**

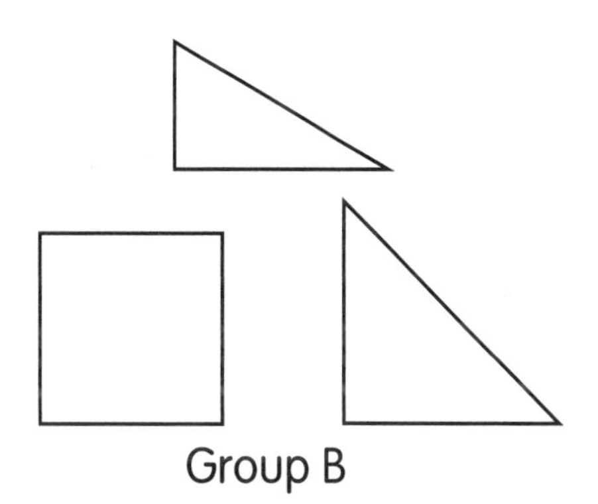

Group A

Group B

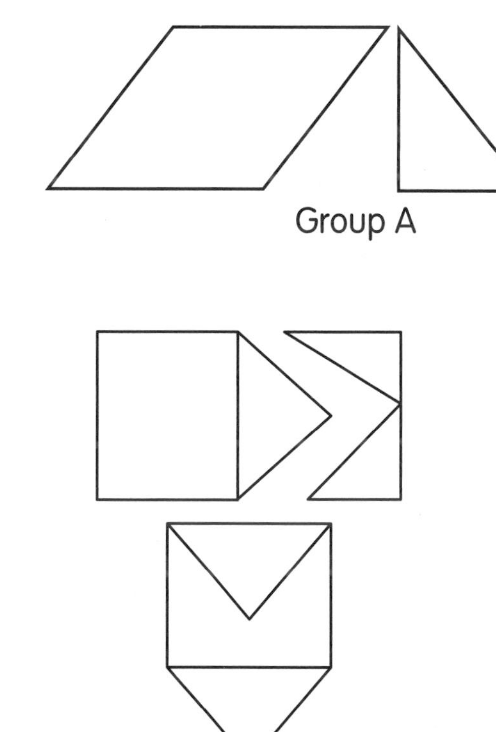

Group C

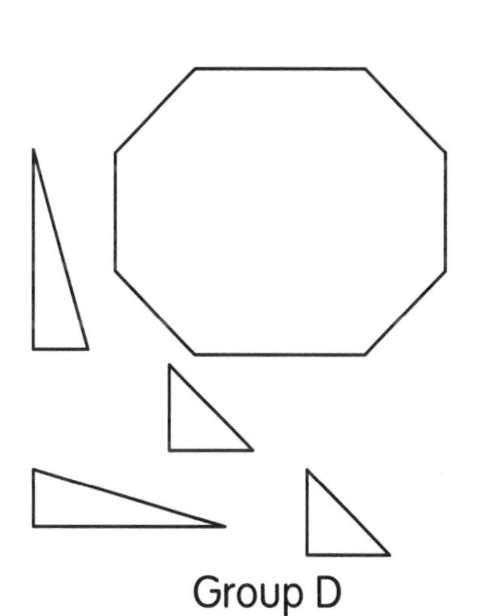

Group D

Name: ______________________ Date: ______________

**2.** Jason made 4 charts to show the different sizes of each type of shape.
Use the clues to guess the type of shape on each chart.
Draw the shapes in the boxes below.

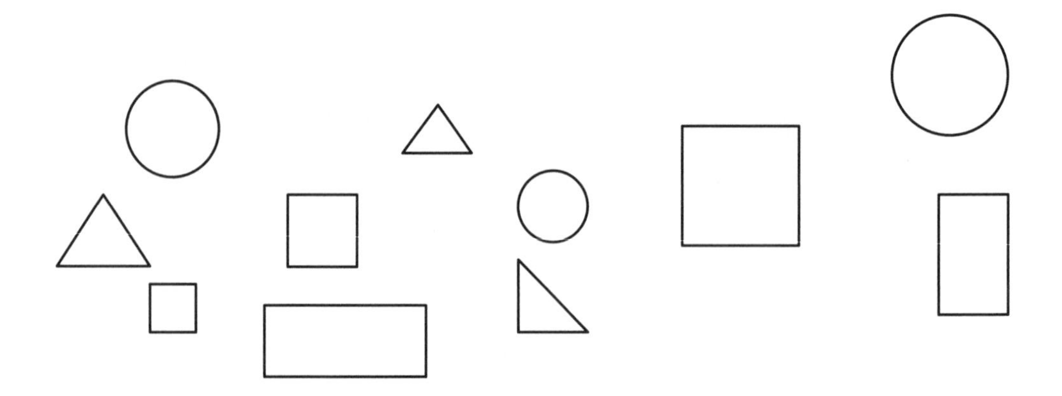

**CLUES**

The triangles chart is next to the squares chart.
The triangles chart is not on the left.
The circles chart is between the squares chart and the rectangles chart.

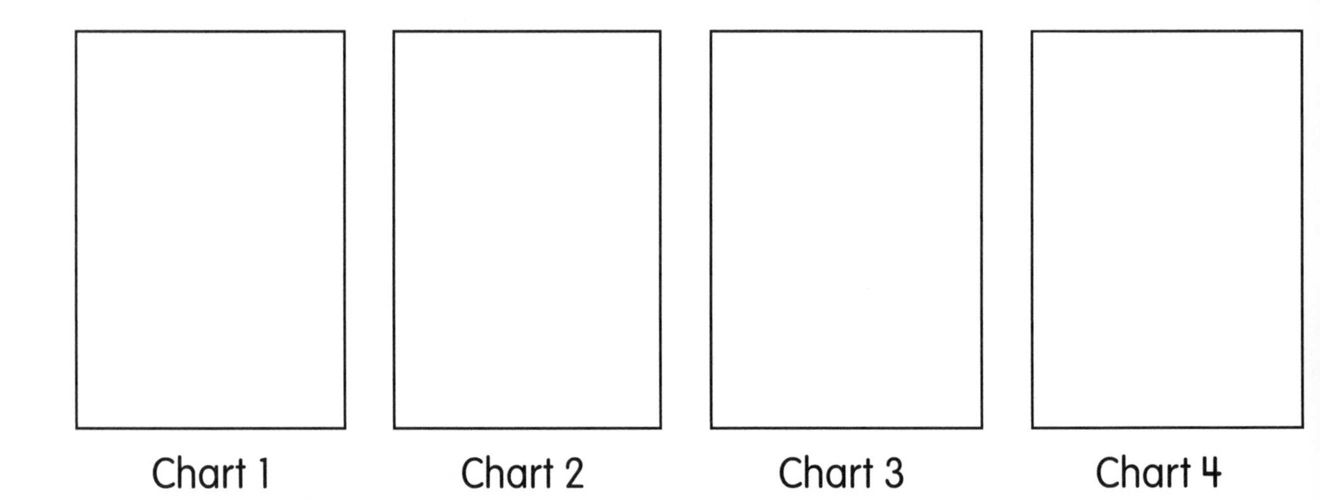

Name: ______________________ Date: ______________

# End-of-Year Test Prep

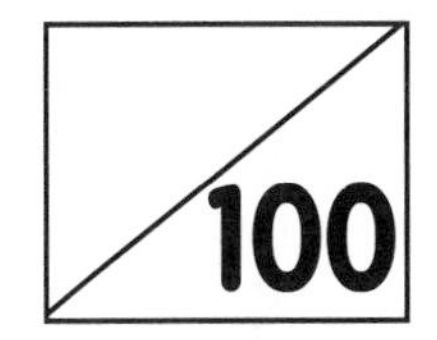


## Multiple Choice (20 × 2 points = 40 points)

**Fill in the circle next to the correct answer.**

**1.** The sum of 563 and 99 is ________.

Ⓐ 460 Ⓑ 620 Ⓒ 660 Ⓓ 662

**2.** ________ – 28 = 380

The missing number is ________.

Ⓐ 322 Ⓑ 368 Ⓒ 408 Ⓓ 480

**3.** Which of the figures are divided equally into two parts?

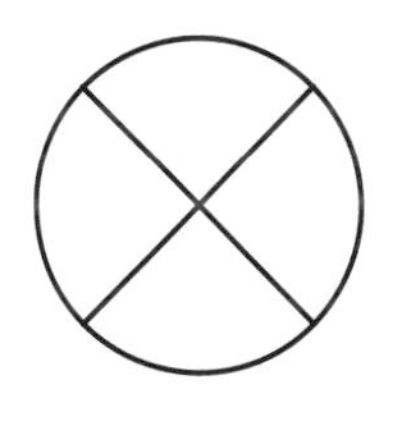
A

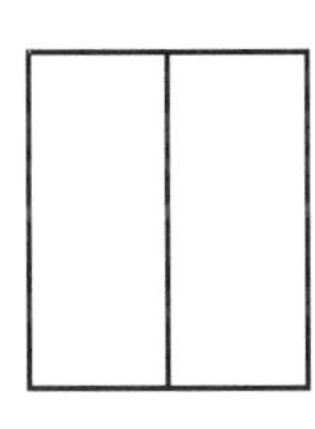
B

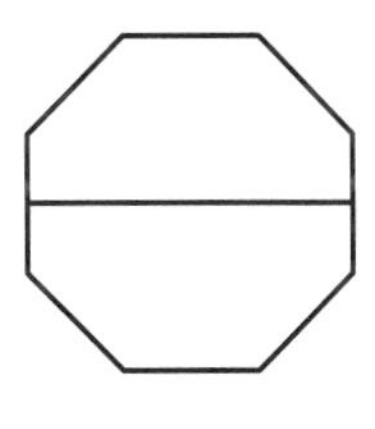
C

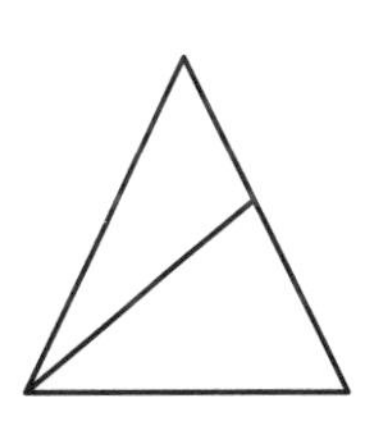
D

Ⓐ A and B Ⓑ B and C

Ⓒ B and D Ⓓ C and D

Name: ______________________ Date: ______________

**4.** Look at the bills and coins.

\+  + 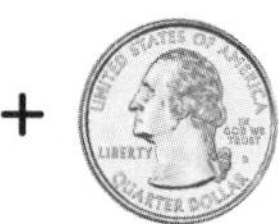 +  + 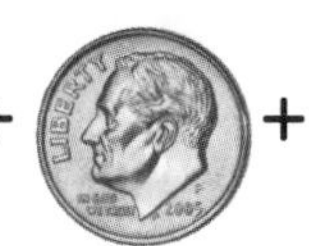 +

What is the amount of money shown?

Ⓐ $20.75 Ⓑ $22.90

Ⓒ $25.65 Ⓓ $28.00

**5.**

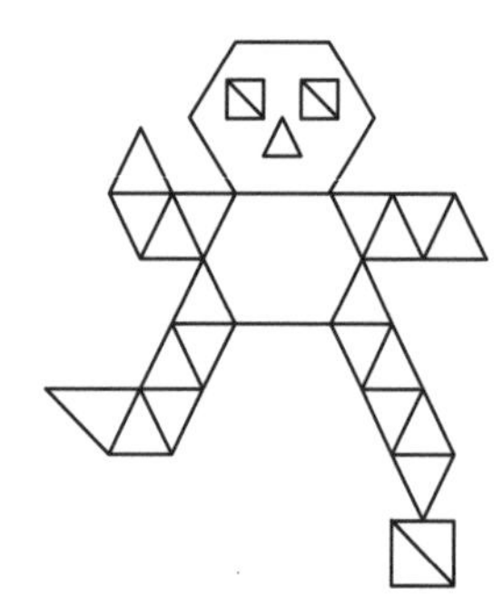

The figure is made up of

__________ and __________.

Ⓐ squares, rectangles Ⓑ squares, triangles

Ⓒ hexagons, triangles Ⓓ rectangles, triangles

**6.** Jim has four coins.
He has 65¢.
There are 2 quarters and a nickel.
What is the amount of the third coin?

Ⓐ 5¢ Ⓑ 10¢ Ⓒ 20¢ Ⓓ $1

Name: ______________________ Date: ______________

**7.** Which of the following groups of fractions is arranged from greatest to least?

(A) $\frac{1}{2}, \frac{1}{3}, \frac{1}{4}$

(B) $\frac{1}{4}, \frac{1}{3}, \frac{1}{2}$

(C) $\frac{1}{3}, \frac{1}{4}, \frac{1}{2}$

(D) $\frac{1}{3}, \frac{1}{2}, \frac{1}{4}$

**8.** Which figure shows $\frac{1}{4}$?

(A)

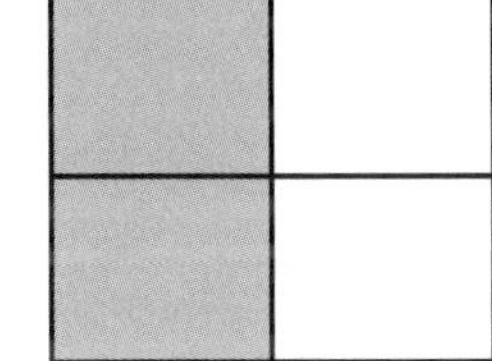

(B)

(C)

(D)

**9.**

The time shown on the clock is __________.

(A) 8:30

(B) 8:00

(C) 7:30

(D) 7:00

Name: ____________________ Date: ____________

**10.**

The time is ________.

It is 30 minutes after ________.

(A) 12:30, 1:00 (B) 1:30, 2:00

(C) 1:00, 12:30 (D) 1:30, 1:00

**11.** How many pitchers can 10 bottles of water fill?

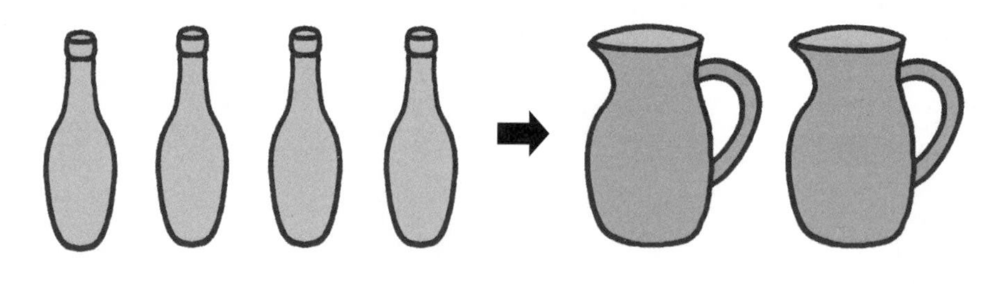

(A) 7 (B) 6 (C) 5 (D) 4

**12.** Container A has ________ liters of water more than Container B.

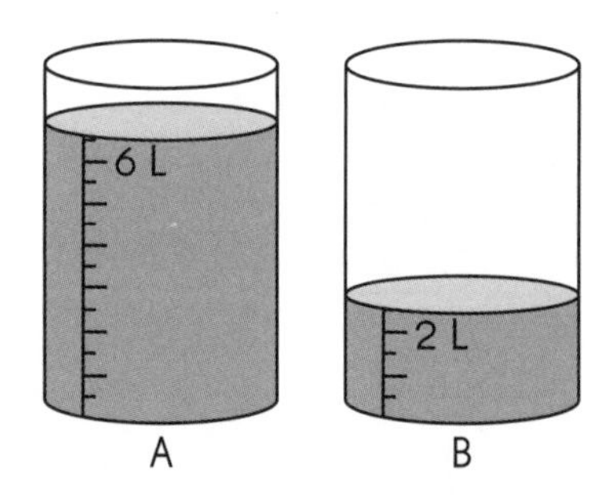


(A) 6 (B) 2 (C) 8 (D) 4

Name: ______________________ Date: ______________

**13.** What comes next in the pattern?

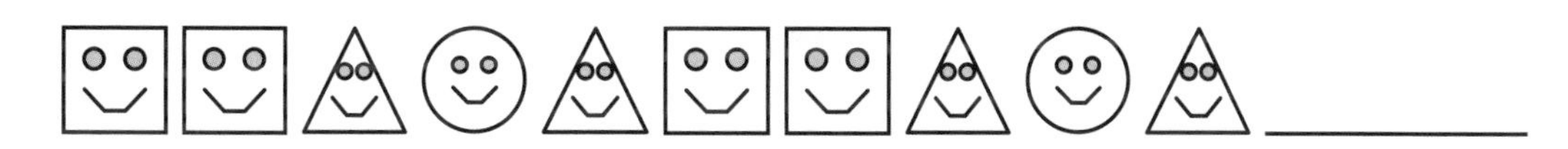

(A)  (B)

(C)  (D)

**14.** Which figure is made up of 2 curves and 3 parts of lines?

(A) 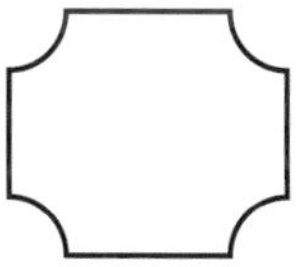 (B)

(C) 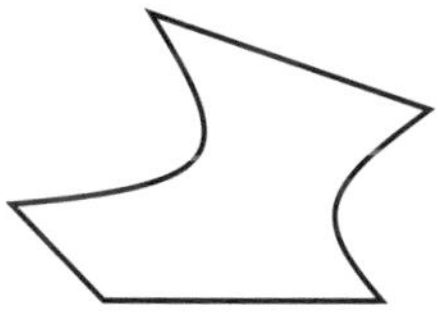 (D)

**15.** Which object has only 2 flat surfaces?

(A)  (B)

(C)  (D)

Name: ______________________ Date: ______________

**16.** The figure is made up of a ________ and 2 ________.

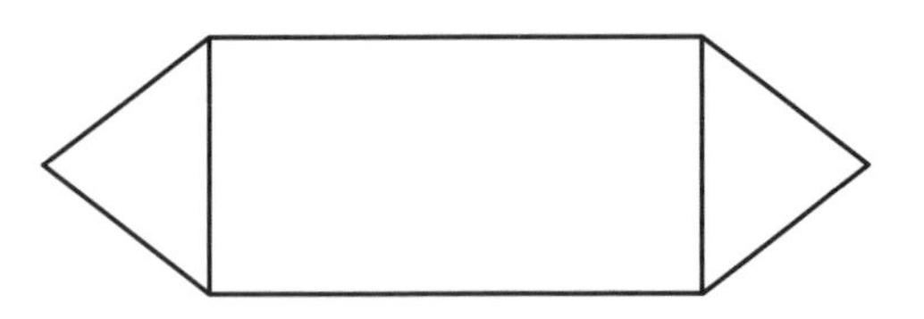

Ⓐ rectangle, circles

Ⓑ square, circles

Ⓒ rectangle, triangles

Ⓓ circle, triangles

**17.** Paul has 3 bags of carrots.
Each bag has 4 carrots.
How many carrots does he have in all?

Ⓐ 3 Ⓑ 4 Ⓒ 7 Ⓓ 12

**18.** What fraction of the figure is shaded?

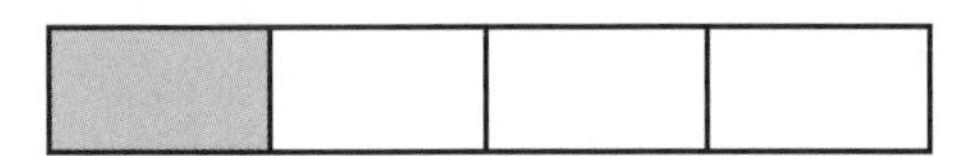

Ⓐ $\frac{1}{2}$ Ⓑ $\frac{1}{4}$

Ⓒ $\frac{3}{4}$ Ⓓ $\frac{6}{8}$

Name: ______________________ Date: ______________

The picture graph shows how some students in a class get to school.

**How Some Students Get to School**

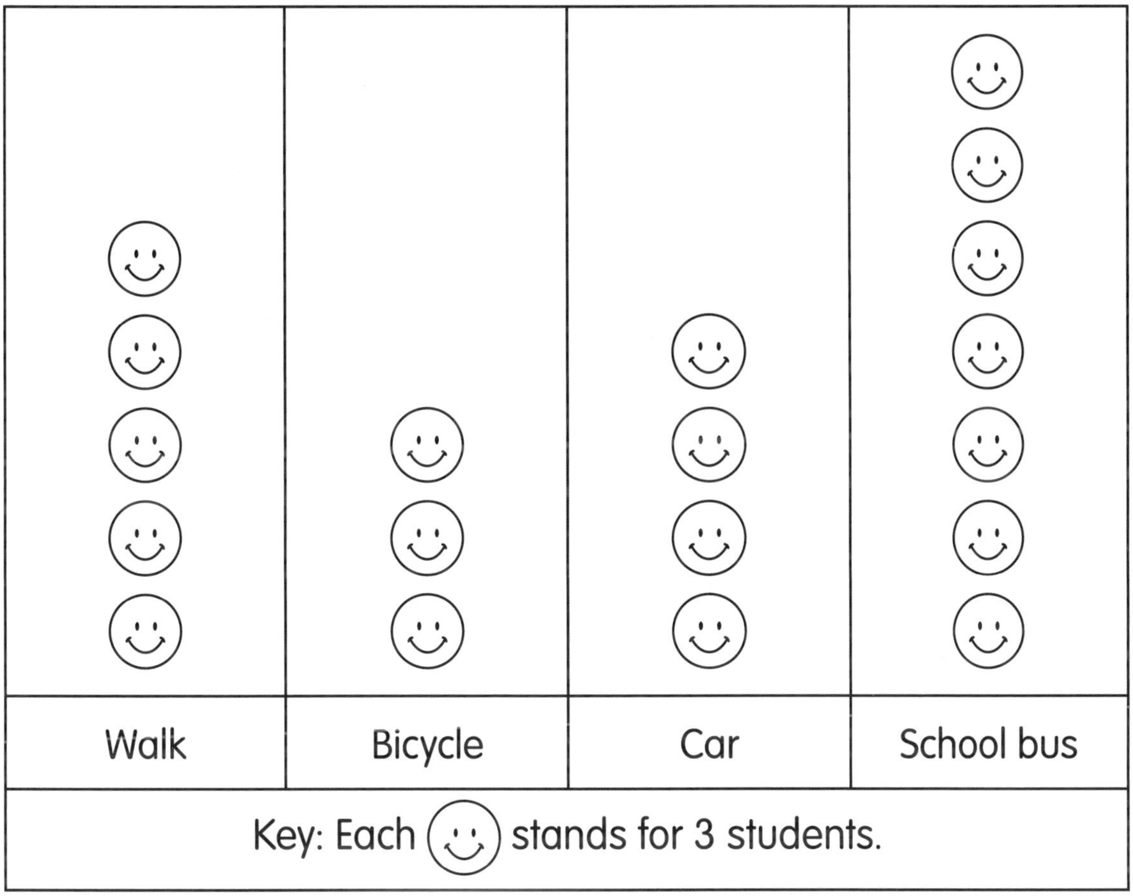

| Walk | Bicycle | Car | School bus |
|---|---|---|---|
| ☺ ☺ ☺ ☺ ☺ | ☺ ☺ ☺ | ☺ ☺ ☺ ☺ | ☺ ☺ ☺ ☺ ☺ ☺ ☺ |

Key: Each ☺ stands for 3 students.

**Use the picture graph to answer these questions.**

**19.** How many students walk to school?

Ⓐ 10  Ⓑ 15  Ⓒ 20  Ⓓ 25

**20.** 12 girls take the bus to school.
How many boys take the bus to school?

Ⓐ 9  Ⓑ 10  Ⓒ 3  Ⓓ 12

Name: ______________________ Date: ______________

## Short Answer (20 × 2 points = 40 points)

**Follow the directions.**

**21.** Subtract.

$825 - 299 =$ ________

**22.** Solve.

Cindy decorates the room with 27 blue bows and 43 red bows. How many bows are there in all?

There are ________ bows in all.

**23.** Draw the hands on the clock to show the correct time.

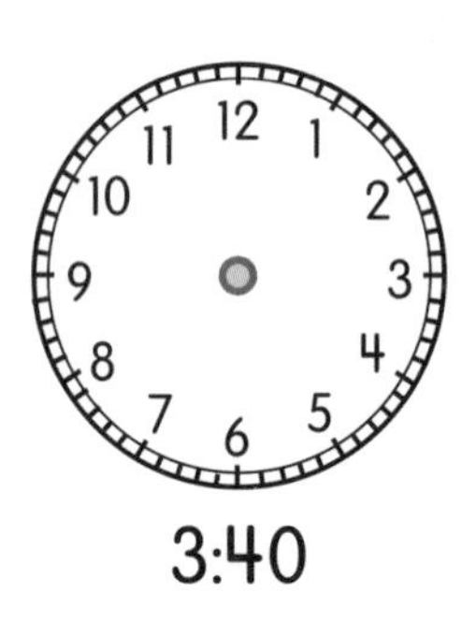


3:40

**24.** Fill in the blank.

Mother puts the cake in the oven at 2:30.

She takes it out of the oven 1 hour later.

What time does she take the cake out of the oven?

She takes the cake out of the oven at ________.

Name: ______________________ Date: ______________

**25.** Shade $\frac{2}{5}$ of the figure below.

**26.** Write the amount of money.

$______

**27.** Circle the greatest amount of money.

$30.95 $35.00 $32.50

**28.** Solve.
Sam collects 46 seashells on Monday.
He collects 58 seashells on Tuesday.
How many more seashells does Sam collect on Tuesday than on Monday?

Sam collects ______ more seashells on Tuesday than on Monday.

**Name:** ______________________________ **Date:** ________________

**29.** Draw a bar model to help you solve.
Belle shares 25 erasers equally with 5 friends.
How many erasers does each friend get?

Each friend gets ________ erasers.

**30.** Use the inch ruler to find the missing numbers.

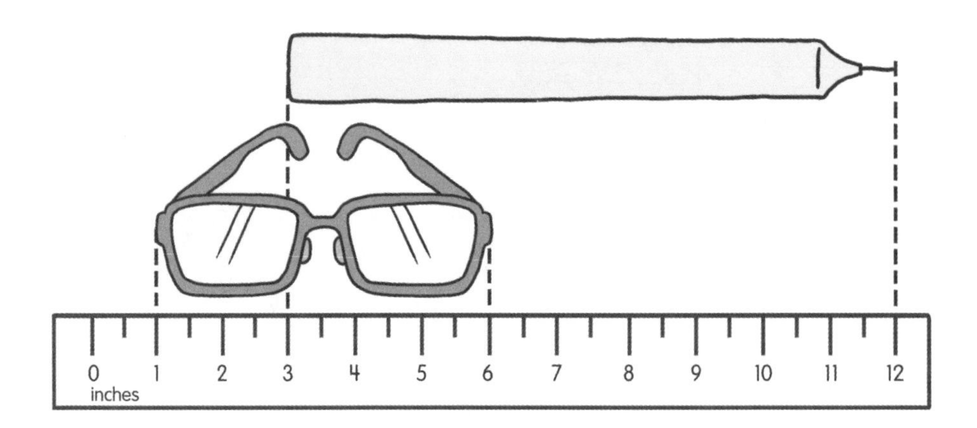


**a.** The pair of glasses is ________ inches long.

**b.** The candle is ________ inches longer than the pair of glasses.

Name: ______________________ Date: ______________

**31.** Find the missing numbers.

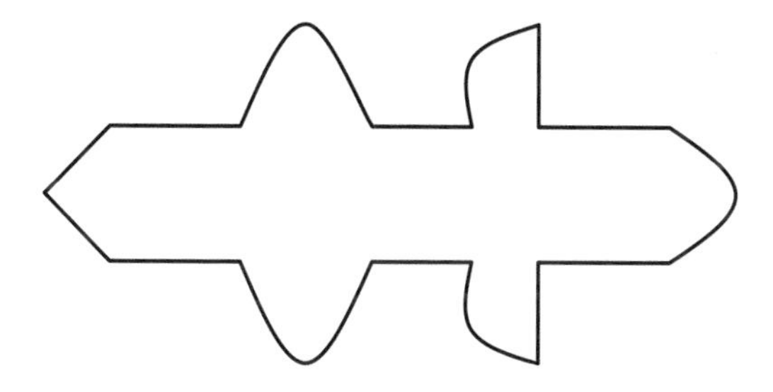

The picture is made with ________ parts of lines

and ________ curves.

**32.** Draw a bar model to help you solve.
Leon, Jenny, Donna, and Mary receive $5 each.
How much money do they receive in all?

They receive $________ in all.

**33.** Draw the time correctly on the clock.

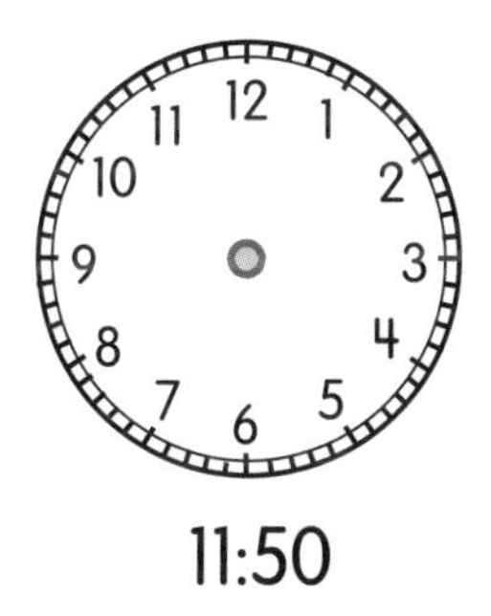


11:50

Name: ______________________ Date: ______________

**34.** Sam leaves his home at 6:30.
He reaches his friend's house after 1 hour.
What time does he reach his friend's house?

He reaches his friend's house at ________.

**35.** Study the pattern.
Draw the figure that comes next.

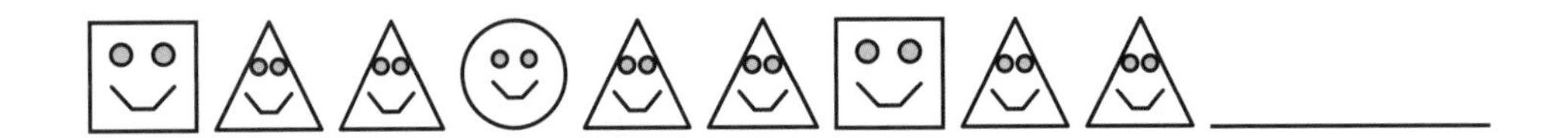

**36.** Peter has a can of soup.
If he traces the bottom of the can on paper, what shape will he get?

He will get a ________.

**37.** If ☺ stands for 3 children, ☺ ☺ ☺ ☺

stands for ________ children.

Name: ______________________________ Date: ____________________

Use the pictures to answer questions 38 and 39.

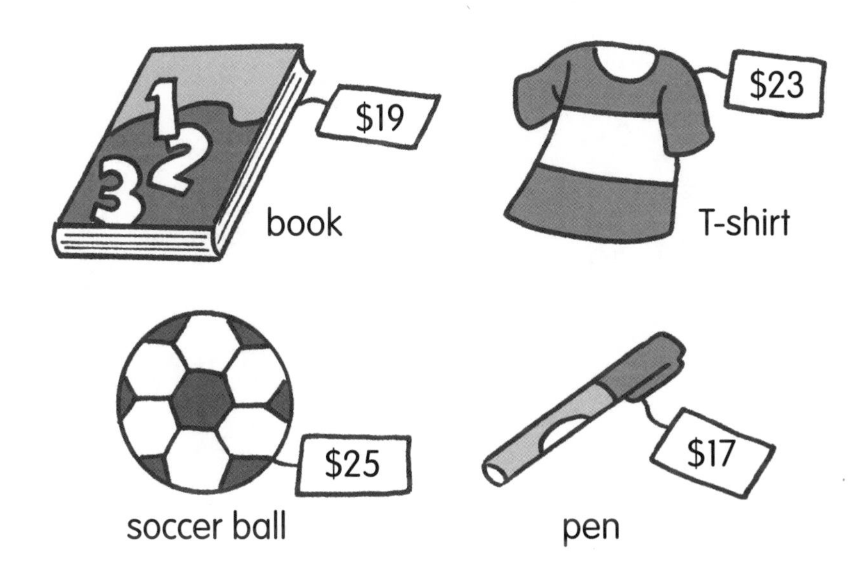


**38.** Shelly spends exactly $36 on two of the items.
Which items does she buy?

She buys a __________ and a __________.

**39.** Johnny has $45.
He wants to buy two soccer balls and a T-shirt.
How much more money does he need?

He needs $__________ more.

**40.**

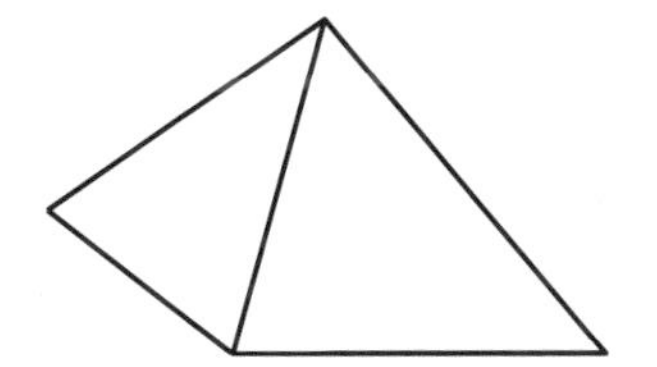

A pyramid has __________ flat surfaces.

Name: ____________________ Date: ____________________

# Extended Response (5 × 4 points = 20 points)

**Solve.**

**Draw bar models to help you.**

**41.** Joel has 682 stamps.
His uncle gives him 239 more stamps.
How many stamps does he have in all?

He has ________ stamps in all.

**42.** Lionel buys 24 stickers to decorate 4 charts.
He puts an equal number of stickers on each chart.
How many stickers does he put on each chart?

He puts ________ stickers on each chart.

Name: ______________________ Date: ______________

**43.** I eat $\frac{1}{3}$ of a muffin.
Jenny eats $\frac{1}{3}$ of a muffin.
What fraction of the muffin is left?

________ of the muffin is left.

**44.** Box A has 350 marbles.
Box B has 128 marbles more than Box A.
Box C has 45 marbles less than Box B.
How many marbles are in Box C?

There are ________ marbles in Box C.

Name: ______________________ Date: ______________

**45.** The line plot shows the number of goals scored by each player in a soccer competition.
Each ✗ represents one player.

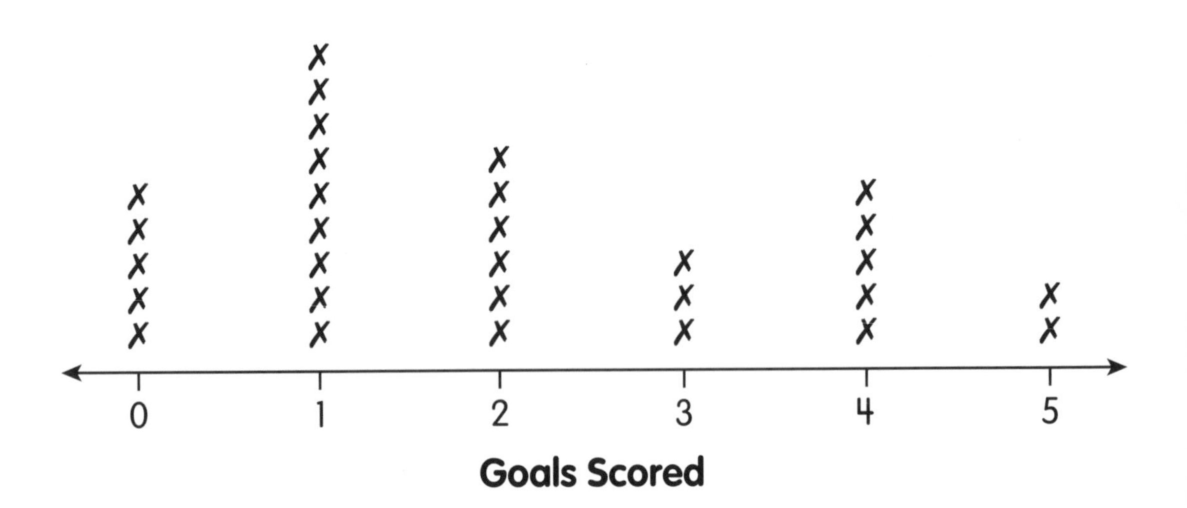


**a.** Use the line plot to complete the table.

| Number of goals | 0 | 1 | 2 | 3 | 4 | 5 |
|---|---|---|---|---|---|---|
| Number of players | | | | | | |

**Fill in the blanks.**
**Use the data in the line plot or the table.**

**b.** __________ players were in the soccer competition.

**c.** The number of goals scored by most players is __________.

**d.** __________ players scored at least 5 goals.

# Answers

## Chapter 10

**Lesson 1**

1. The sum of 512 and 350 is 862.
2. The sum of 469 and 108 is 577.
3. The sum of 275 and 354 is 629.
4. $240 + $550 = $790
   The sum of money they save is $790.
5. 529 + 360 = 889
   The sum of the two numbers is 889.

**Lesson 2**

1. 27 2. 69 3. 89
4. 39 5. 59 6. 77
7. 45 – 4 = 41
   So, 35 + 6 = 41.
8. 67 + 10 = 77
   77 – 5 = 72
   So, 67 + 5 = 72.
9. 94 10. 35 11. 52 12. 62
13. 6 + 2 = 8
    230 + 8 = 238
    So, 236 + 2 = 238.
14. 475 15. 768 16. 268 17. 369
18. 549 + 10 = 559
    559 – 3 = 556
    So, 549 + 7 = 556.
19. 397 20. 461 21. 365 22. 160
23. 20 + 30 = 50
    405 + 50 = 455
    So, 425 + 30 = 455.
24. 766 25. 599 26. 697 27. 865
28. 677 + 100 = 777
    777 – 40 = 737
    So, 677 + 60 = 737.
29. 421 30. 954 31. 866 32. 532
33. 200 + 200 = 400
    400 + 67 = 467
    So, 267 + 200 = 467.
34. 551 35. 964 36. 908 37. 882

**Lesson 3**

1. The difference between 82 and 37 is 45.
2. The difference between 650 and 420 is 230.
3. The difference between 900 and 575 is 325.
4. 450 – 230 = 220
   The difference is 220 burgers.
5. 150 – 77 = 73
   The difference is 73 muffins.

**Lesson 4**

1. 27 2. 46 3. 61
4. 50 5. 72 6. 82
7. 53 – 10 = 43
   43 + 1 = 44
   So, 53 – 9 = 44.
8. 74 – 10 = 64
   64 + 4 = 68
   So, 74 – 6 = 68.
9. 54 10. 23 11. 34 12. 89
13. 6 – 5 = 1
    530 + 1 = 531
    So, 536 – 5 = 531.
14. 684 15. 822 16. 528 17. 482
18. 473 – 10 = 463
    463 + 5 = 468
    So, 473 – 5 = 468.
19. 756 20. 812 21. 418 22. 644
23. 90 – 30 = 60
    402 + 60 = 462
    So, 492 – 30 = 462.
24. 226 25. 713 26. 248 27. 617
28. 361 – 100 = 261
    261 + 30 = 291
    So, 361 – 70 = 291.
29. 440 30. 190 31. 480 32. 730
33. 400 – 200 = 200
    200 + 28 = 228
    So, 428 – 200 = 228.
34. 345 35. 231 36. 380 37. 205

**Lesson 5**

1. 16 is nearer to 20 than to 10.
   16 is about 20 when rounded to the nearest ten.
2. 23 is nearer to 20 than to 30.
   23 is about 20 when rounded to the nearest ten.
3. 32 is nearer to 30 than to 40.
   32 is about 30 when rounded to the nearest ten.

4. 44 is nearer to 40 than to 50.
   44 is about 40 when rounded to the nearest ten.
5. 78 is between 70 and 80.
6. 91 is between 90 and 100.
7. 458 is between 450 and 460.
8. 853 is between 850 and 860.
9. 425 is about 430.
10. 652 is about 650.
11. 856 is about 860.
12. 100; 98 is about 100.
13. 130; 125 is about 130.
14. 370; 369 is about 370.
15. 420; 424 is about 420.
16. 650; 652 is about 650.
17. 860; 856 is about 860.
18. The greatest amount the camera could cost is $54.
    The least amount the camera could cost is $45.
19. The greatest length the pool could be is 84 meters.
    The least length the pool could be is 75 meters.
20. The greatest mass the rice could be is 504 grams.
    The least mass the rice could be is 495 grams.
21. 268 + 323 = 591
    268 is about 270.
    323 is about 320.
    270 + 320 = 590
    So, 268 + 323 is about 590.
    Yes, because 590 is close to 591.
22. 479 – 124 = 355
    479 is about 480.
    124 is about 120.
    480 – 120 = 360
    So, 479 – 124 is about 360.
    Yes, because 360 is close to 355.
23. 235 + 552 = 787
    Check: 240 + 550 = 790
    Yes, because 790 is close to 787.
24. 574 – 296 = 278
    Check: 570 – 300 = 270
    Yes, because 270 is close to 278.
25. a. $38 is $40 when rounded to the nearest ten.
    b. $11 is $10 when rounded to the nearest ten.
    c. $27 is $30 when rounded to the nearest ten.
    d. $18 is $20 when rounded to the nearest ten.
    The estimated total cost is $100.
    Yes.

**Put on Your Thinking Cap!**

1. Thinking skill: Analyzing parts and whole
   Strategy: Make a systematic list
   Solution:

| 19 | 18 | 17 | 16 | 15 | 14 | 13 | 12 | 11 | 10 |
|---|---|---|---|---|---|---|---|---|---|
| 1 | 2 | 3 | 4 | 5 | 6 | 7 | 8 | 9 | 10 |

   13 – 7 = 6
   The numbers are 13 and 7.
2. Thinking skill: Identifying patterns and relationships
   Strategy: Look for patterns
   Solution: 8 + 16 = 24
   24 + 20 = 44
   The missing numbers are 24 and 44.

## Chapter 11

**Lesson 1**

1. Circle five $1 bills.
2. Circle two $5 bills.
3. Circle a $10 bill and two $5 bills.
4. Circle 3 quarters, 2 dimes, and a nickel.
5. Circle 2 quarters, 4 dimes, a nickel, and 5 pennies.
6. more than
7. less than
8. equal to
9. $24
10. $25.25
11. $0.45
12. $37
13. $98.03
14. 0 dollars 6 cents
15. 2 dollars 33 cents
16. 10 dollars 28 cents
17. 24 dollars 74 cents
18. 40 dollars 52 cents
19. Ben has 25 dollars and 75 cents or $25.75.
20. Sheena has 12 dollars and 37 cents or $12.37.
21. 53¢ or $0.53
22. 68¢ or $0.68
23. 726¢ or $7.26
24. 3085¢ or $30.85
25. 3167¢ or $31.67
26. $2.36

27. $3.27
28. $0.28
29. $6.80
30. $1.15
31. $4.25
32. 163¢
33. 400¢
34. 348¢
35. 560¢
36. 70¢
37. 916¢

**Lesson 2**

1.

| Dollars | Cents |
|---|---|
| 12 | 30 |

| Dollars | Cents |
|---|---|
| 17 | 50 |

$17.50 is more than $12.30.
$12.30 is less than $17.50.

2.

| Dollars | Cents |
|---|---|
| 45 | 62 |

| Dollars | Cents |
|---|---|
| 45 | 40 |

$45.62 is more than $45.40.
$45.40 is less than $45.62.

3.

| Dollars | Cents |
|---|---|
| 25 | 45 |

| Dollars | Cents |
|---|---|
| 25 | 60 |

| Dollars | Cents |
|---|---|
| 26 | 50 |

No.
$26.50 is the greatest amount.
$25.45 is the least amount.

4.

| Dollars | Cents |
|---|---|
| 44 | 70 |

| Dollars | Cents |
|---|---|
| 43 | 70 |

| Dollars | Cents |
|---|---|
| 44 | 75 |

No.
$44.75 is the greatest amount.
$43.70 is the least amount.

5. $7.30 ☐ $8.15 ☑
6. $22.05 ☐ $27 ☑
7. Circle $3.60
8. Circle $13.45
9. Circle $33.98
10. Circle $65.80
11. Circle $7.50
12. Circle $70.70
13. $2.08
14. $28.00
15. $2.08, $2.80, $28.00

**Lesson 3**

1. 13¢ 10¢
?¢

13¢ + 10¢ = 23¢
$1 = 100¢

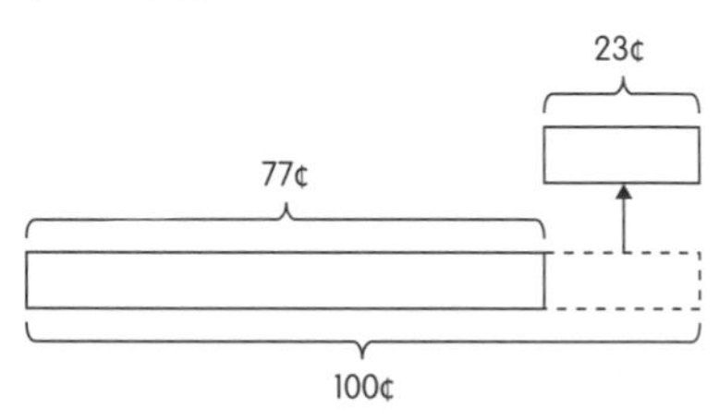


100¢ – 23¢ = 77¢
Gary gets 77¢ change.

2.

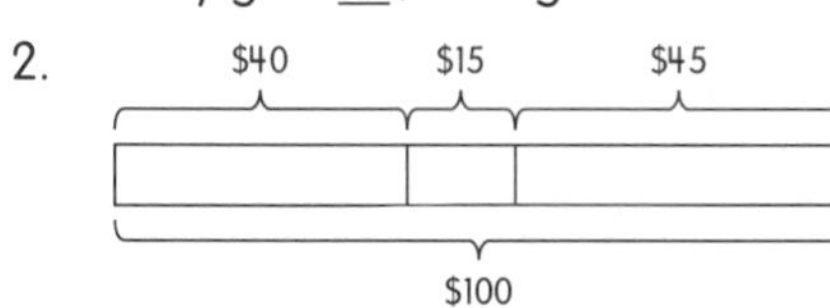


$100 – $40 – $15 = $45
Mrs. Jimenez has $45 left.

3.

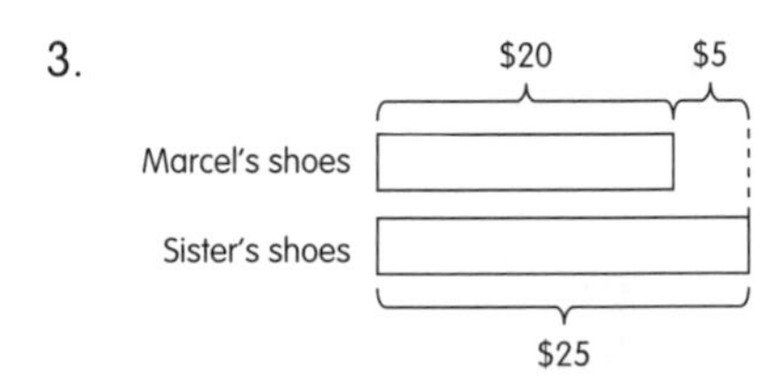


$20 + $5 = $25
His sister's pair of shoes costs $25.

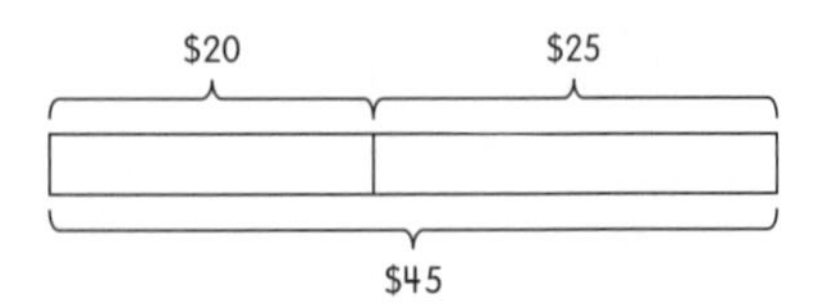


$20 + $25 = $45
They pay $45 in all.

4.

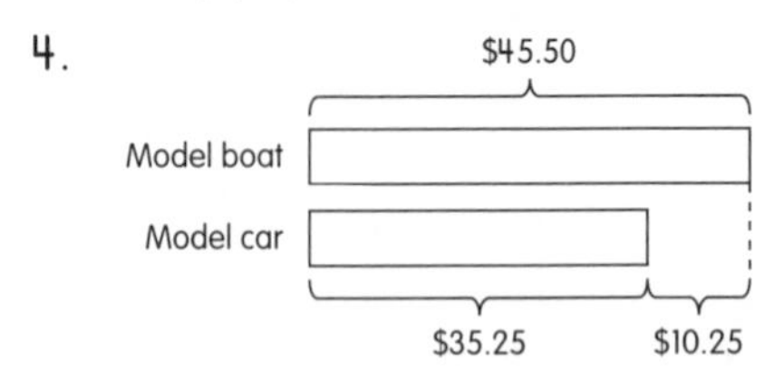


$45.50 – $10.25 = $35.25
The model car costs $35.25.

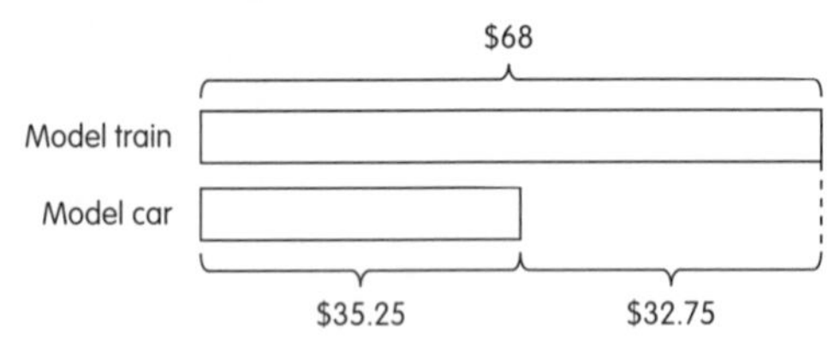


$68 – $35.25 = $32.75
The model train costs $32.75 more than the model car.

5.

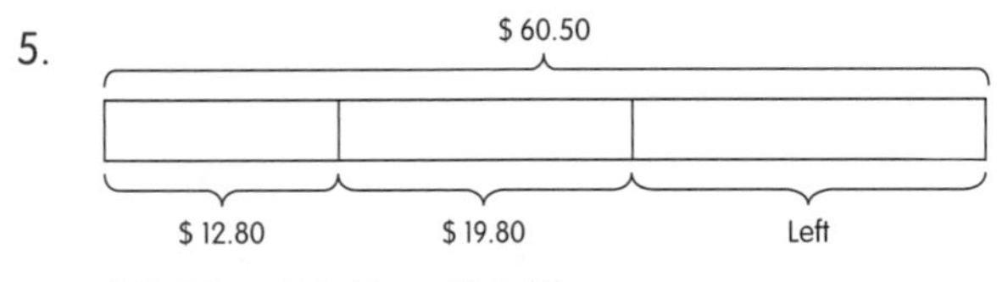


$12.80 + $19.80 = $32.60
$60.50 – $32.60 = $27.90
Twyla has $27.90 left.

6.

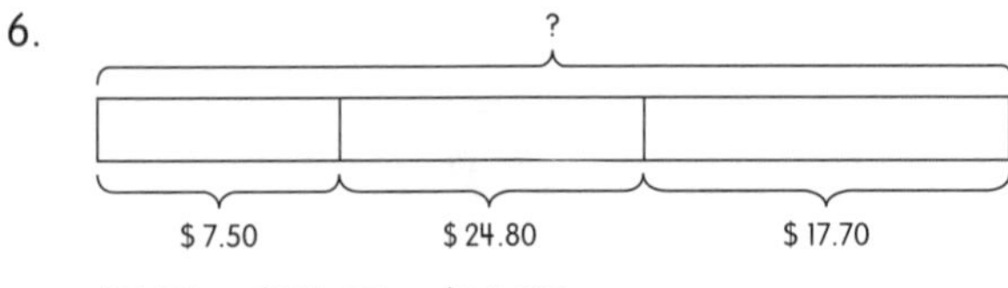


$7.50 + $24.80 = $32.30
$32.30 + $17.70 = $50.00
Carmen had $50.00 at the beginning.

7.

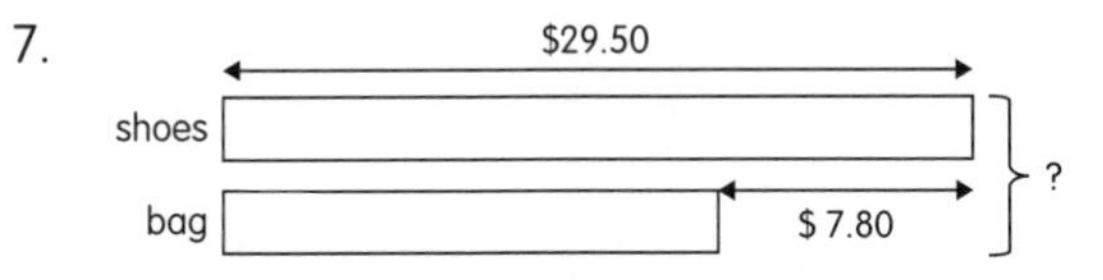


$29.50 – $7.80 = $21.70
$29.50 + $21.70 = $51.20
Rain pays $51.20 for these two items.

8.

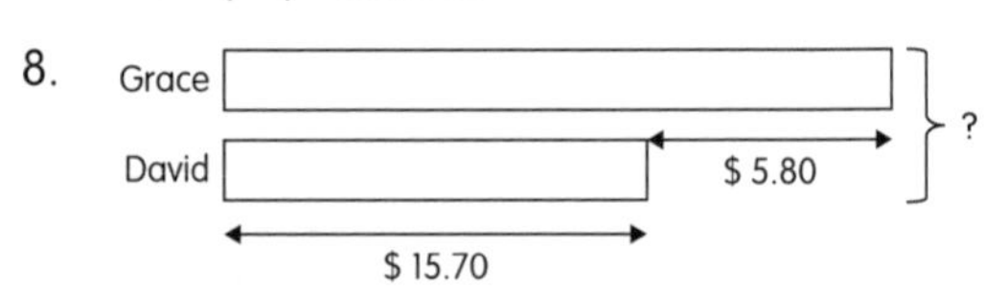


$15.70 + $5.80 = $21.50
$15.70 + $21.50 = $37.20
The present costs $37.20.

**Put on Your Thinking Cap!**

1. Thinking skill: Classifying
   Strategy: Make a systematic list
   Solution:
   Mr. & Mrs. Brown: 2 × $8 = $16
   9-year-old & 6-year-old: 2 × $4 = $8
   2-year-old: free
   $16 + $8 = $24
   The family spent $24 on the tickets in all.
2. Thinking skill: Deduction
   Strategy: Use guess and check
   Solution: $34.80 + $15 = $49.80
   She bought the toaster and the handbag.

## Chapter 12

**Lesson 1**

1.

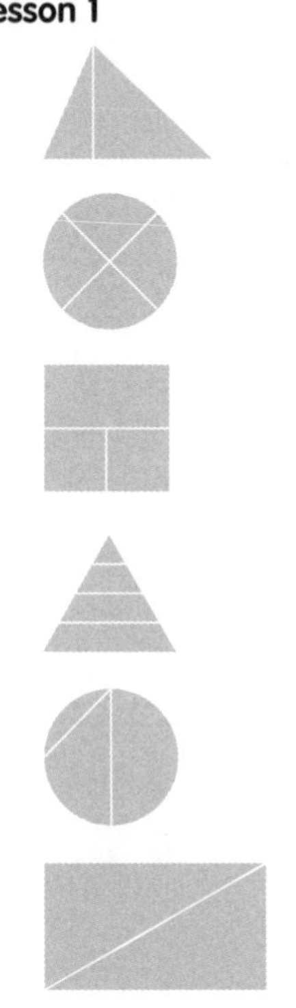

2. Circle $\frac{1}{3}$, one-third

3. Circle one-quarter

4. Circle one-half

5. 1, 4; $\frac{1}{4}$

6. 1, 3; $\frac{1}{3}$

7. $\frac{1}{4}$

8. $\frac{1}{3}$

9. $\frac{1}{2}$

10. Answers vary.
For example,

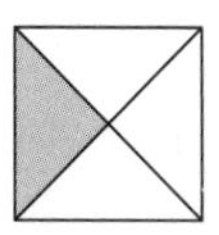

11. Answers vary.
For example,

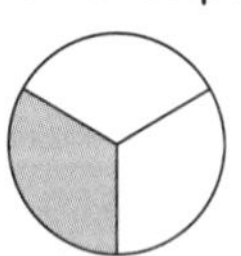

12. Answers vary.
For example,

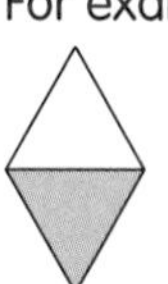

**Lesson 2**

1. $\underline{\frac{1}{2}}$ is shaded.

   $\underline{\frac{1}{3}}$ is shaded.

   $\underline{\frac{1}{2}}$ is greater than $\underline{\frac{1}{3}}$.

   $\underline{\frac{1}{3}}$ is less than $\underline{\frac{1}{2}}$.

2. $\underline{\frac{1}{3}}$ is shaded.

   $\underline{\frac{1}{4}}$ is shaded.

   $\underline{\frac{1}{3}}$ is greater than $\underline{\frac{1}{4}}$.

   $\underline{\frac{1}{4}}$ is less than $\underline{\frac{1}{3}}$.

3. $\underline{\frac{1}{4}}$ is shaded.

   $\underline{\frac{1}{2}}$ is shaded.

   $\underline{\frac{1}{2}}$ is greater than $\underline{\frac{1}{4}}$.

   $\underline{\frac{1}{4}}$ is less than $\underline{\frac{1}{2}}$.

4. $\frac{1}{2} \geq \frac{1}{3}$

   $\frac{1}{3} \leq \frac{1}{2}$

5. $\frac{1}{4} \leq \frac{1}{2}$

   $\frac{1}{2} \geq \frac{1}{4}$

6. $\frac{1}{2}, \frac{1}{3}, \frac{1}{4}$

**Lesson 3**

1. $\frac{1}{2}$ or $\frac{2}{4}$

2. $\frac{1}{2}$ or $\frac{2}{4}$

3. $\frac{4}{4}$

4. 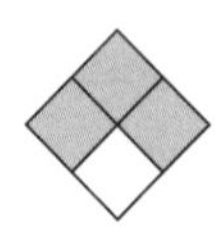

5.

6.

7. $\frac{1}{4} + \frac{2}{4} = \frac{3}{4}$

8. $\frac{1}{3} + \frac{1}{3} = \frac{2}{3}$

9. $\frac{1}{2} + \frac{1}{2} = 1$

10.

11.

12.

13. $1 - \frac{2}{4} = \underline{\frac{2}{4}}$

14. $\frac{2}{3} - \frac{1}{3} = \underline{\frac{1}{3}}$

15. $1 - \frac{1}{2} = \underline{\frac{1}{2}}$

16. $\frac{3}{4} - \frac{2}{4} = \underline{\frac{1}{4}}$

**Put on Your Thinking Cap!**

1. Thinking skill: Spatial visualization
   Strategy: Use a diagram
   Solution: a. Color $\frac{1}{4}$ of the pizza.

   He ate $\underline{\frac{1}{4}}$ of the pizza.

   b. $\underline{\frac{3}{4}}$ of the pizza is left.

2. Thinking skill: Spatial visuaization
   Strategy: Use a diagram
   Solution: He must color 3 more stars.

## Chapter 13

**Lesson 1**

1. less
2. more

| | Less than 1 foot | More than 1 foot |
|---|---|---|
| 3. | ✔ | |
| 4. | | ✔ |
| 5. | ✔ | |
| 6. | ✔ | |

**Lesson 2**

1. Circle the textbook.
2. Circle the trash bin.
3. Circle the handbag.
4. a. Ribbon A  b. 2
5. a. B  b. 5  c. 6

**Lesson 3**

1. 2  2. 3  3. 4  4. 5
5. 6  6. 2  7. 5  8. 9

**Lesson 4**

1. 6  2. 5
3. 4  4. 2
5. 3  6. 2
7. pen  8. paper clip
9. 7 inches  10. 5 inches; pen
11. 12 inches; 1 foot  12. rope; stick
13. scissors and pen, pencil, paint brush, stick, rope

**Lesson 5**

1. 16 – 12 = 4
   The length of the lace that she has left is 4 feet.
2. 9 + 9 + 9 = 27
   The total length of the sticks is 27 inches.
3. a. 19 – 8 = 11
      The length of the second jump rope is 11 feet.
   b. 11 – 8 = 3
      The second jump rope is 3 feet longer than the first jump rope.
4. 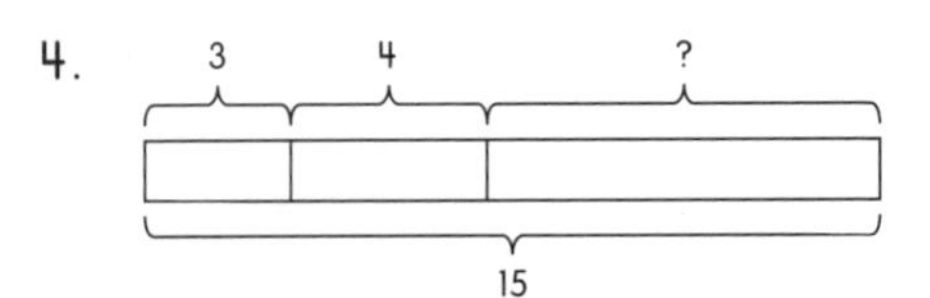

   15 – 3 – 4 = 8
   Ally has 8 feet of cloth left.
5. 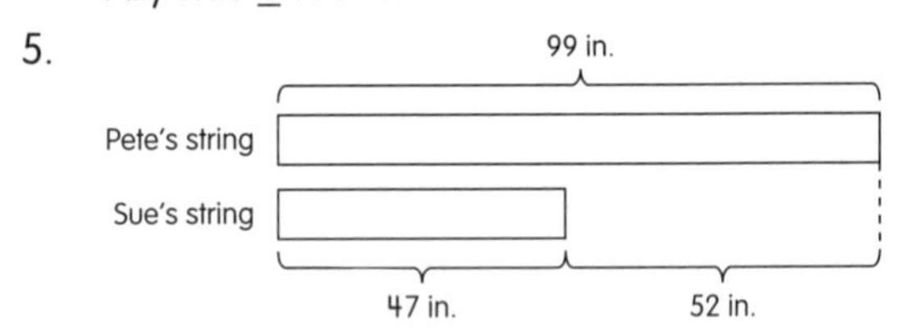

   99 – 47 = 52
   Pete's string of lights is 52 inches longer than Sue's string of lights.

**Put on Your Thinking Cap!**

1. Thinking skill: Comparing
   Strategy: Use a diagram
   Solution:
   Amy
   Sara
   Molly
   Jessica
   Amy, Jessica, Molly, Sara

## Chapter 14

**Lesson 1**

1. 45  2. 15  3. 10  4. 25
5. 
6. 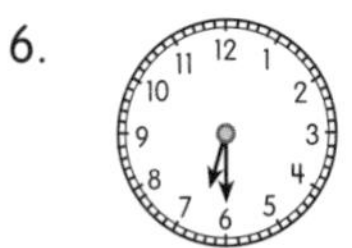
7. 

**Lesson 2**

1. five ten or ten minutes after 5
2. ten thirty-five or thirty-five minutes after 10
3. twelve twenty or twenty minutes after 12
4. four thirty-five or thirty-five minutes after 4
5. one thirty or thirty minutes after 1

6. nine thirty-five or thirty-five minutes after 9
7. three forty or forty minutes after 3
8. seven fifty-five or fifty-five minutes after 7

9.

10. 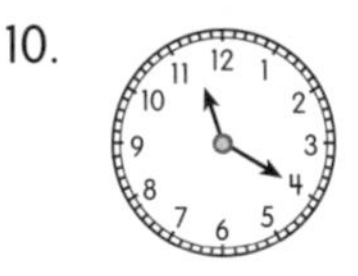

11.

12. 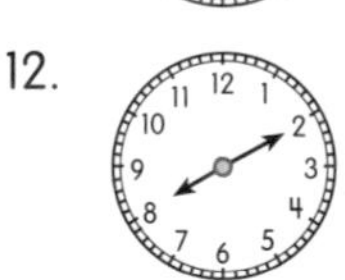

13. three fifteen
14. nine twenty
15. four thirty
16. six forty-five

17.

18.

19. 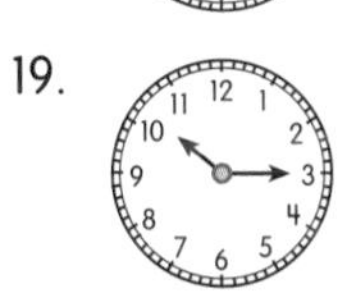

**Lesson 3**

| 1. P.M. | 2. A.M. | 3. A.M. | 4. P.M. |
|---|---|---|---|
| 5. P.M. | 6. P.M. | 7. P.M. | 8. A.M. |
| 9. P.M. | 10. A.M. | | |

11. Jack helps his mother sell food at 6:30 P.M. (5)
Jack eats his breakfast at 7:30 A.M. (1)
Jack goes to the market to buy groceries at 8:30 A.M. (2)
Jack prepares dinner for his brother at 5:00 P.M. (4)
Jack returns home with his mother at 10:25 P.M. (6)
Jack cooks his lunch at 12:15 P.M. (3)

**Lesson 4**

1. 12:00 2. 4:00 3. 7:00 4. 7:30

5. 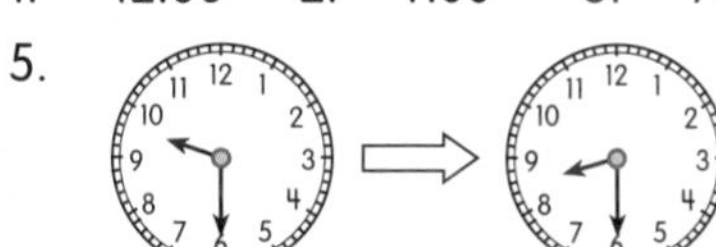

9:30 is 1 hour after 8:30.

6.

10:00 is 1 hour before 11:00.

7.

3:00 is 30 minutes before 3:30.

8. 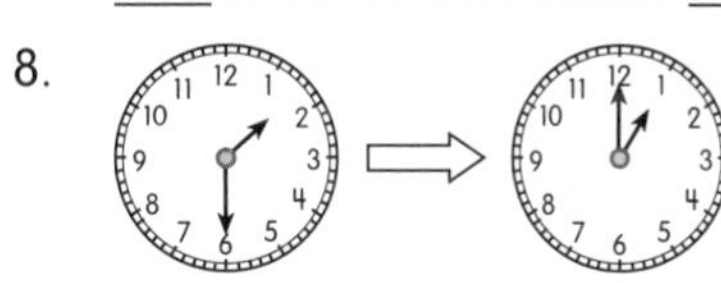

1:30 is 30 minutes after 1:00.

9. 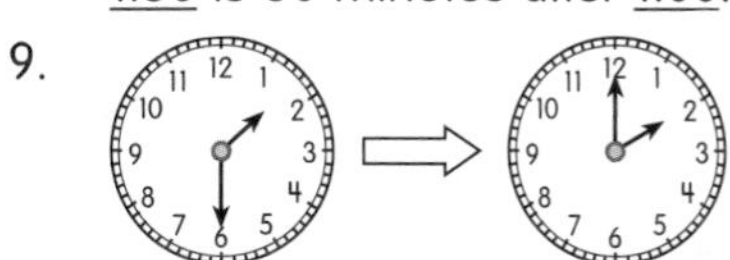

Sandra takes the cake out of the oven at 2:00 P.M.

10. 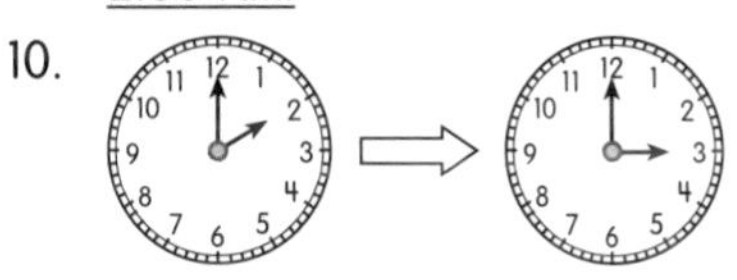

The football practice ends at 3:00 P.M.

11. 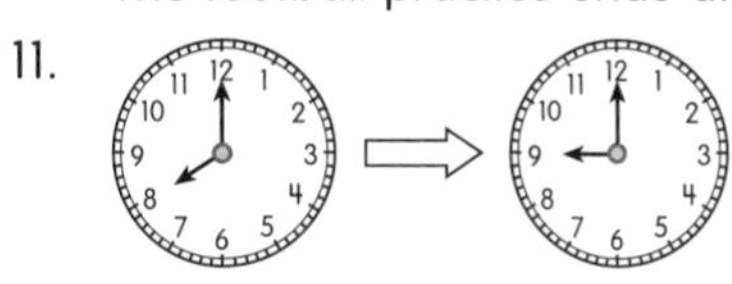

The program ends at 9:00 P.M.

12. before 13. after 14. after 15. after
16. He takes 30 minutes to reach his office.
17. The concert lasts 1 hour.

**Put on Your Thinking Cap!**

1. Thinking skill: Sequencing
Strategy: Solve part of the problem
Solution: Ron takes 1 hour to finish his homework.
Tom starts doing his homework at 7:00 P.M. and finishes his homework at 7:30 P.M.
Tom takes 30 minutes to finish his homework.
Jim starts doing his homework at 6:30 P.M. and finishes his homework at 8:30 P.M.
Jim takes 2 hours to finish his homework.
2. Thinking skill: Sequencing
Strategy: Solve part of the problem
Solution: Sam reaches Town B at 9:00 A.M.
Jack reaches Town B at 7:00 A.M.
a. Jack reached Town B first.
b. Jack reached Town B at 7:00 A.M.
c. Sam reached Town B at 9:00 A.M.

## Test Prep

1. C 2. C 3. B 4. A
5. D 6. B 7. A 8. B
9. C 10. C
11. a. 456 b. 392
12. a. $1.70 b. $5.70
13. Circle the bag on the left.
14. $45 – $25 = $20
She has $20 left.
15. 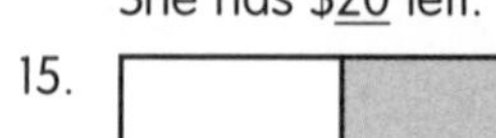
16. $\frac{1}{4}, \frac{2}{4}, \frac{3}{4}, \frac{4}{4}$
17. 
18. 30 minutes 19. 49
20. Circle the 2 $1 bills, 2 quarters, a dime, and a nickel.
21. $4.50 + $5.35 = $9.85
$10 – $9.85 = $0.15
She gets $0.15 change.
22. $125 + $49 = $174
$400 – $174 = $226
They have $226 left.
23. 25 – 18 = 7
She has 7 inches of lace left.
24. 16 + 24 + 25 = 65
The wire was 65 feet long.
25. $\frac{3}{4} - \frac{1}{4} = \frac{2}{4}$
Mrs. Malone reads $\frac{2}{4}$ of the magazine after lunch.
26. 
She finished her dinner at 8:30 P.M.
27. 114 – 33 = 81
81 inches of the fencepost is above the ground.
28. 445 + 56 = 501
445 is about 450.
56 is about 60.
450 + 60 = 510
So, 445 + 56 is about 510.
Yes, 510 is close to 501.

## Chapter 15

**Lesson 1**

1. 18; 18
2. 9, 12, 15, 18, 21, 24
3. 21, 24, 27, 30, 33, 36
4. 5; 15 5. 9; 27
6. 9 7. 18 8. 24 9. 30
10. 3 × $3 = $9
The jars of jam cost $9 in all.
11. 7 × 3 = 21
There are 21 pencils in all.
12. 9 × 3 = 27
There are 27 books in all.
13. 7 × 3 = 21
There are 21 bracelets in all.
14. 10 × 3 = 30
There are 30 fish in all.

**Lesson 2**

1. 5 × 3 = 15
There are 15 pieces of cake in all.
2. 7 × 3 = 21
They have 21 granola bars in all.
3. 3 × 3 = 9
There are 9 pieces of muffin in all.
4. 8 × 3 = 24
There are 24 keys in all.
5. 6 × 3 — 15 + 3
6. 8 × 3 — 30 – 6
7. 10 × 3 — 27 + 3
8. 9 × 3 — 30 – 3
9. 10 × 3 = 30
9 × 3 = 10 groups of 3 – 1 group of 3
= 30 – 3
= 27
10. 7 × 3 = 5 groups of 3 + 2 groups of 3
= 15 + 6
= 21
11. 12; 12 12. 24; 24

**Lesson 3**

1. 8, 12, 16, 20, 24, 28, 32
2. 16, 20, 24, 28, 32, 16, 40
3. 1, 2, 3, 4, 5, 6, 7, 8, 9, 10;
4, 8, 12, 16, 20, 24, 28, 32, 36, 40
4. 4 × 4 = 16
There are 16 stickers in all.

5. $6 \times \$4 = \$24$
   The T-shirts cost $24 in all.

**Lesson 4**

1. $5 \times 4 = 20$
   There are 20 marbles in all.
2. $3 \times 4 = 12$
   She gives 12 cookies in all.
3. $8 \times 4 = 32$
   There are 32 buttons in all.
4. $4 \times 10 = 40$
   Mr. Vasquez uses 40 flowers in all.
5. $10 \times 4 = 40$
   $8 \times 4 = 10$ groups of $4 - 2$ groups of 4
   $= 40 - 8$
   $= 32$
6. $6 \times 4 = 5$ groups of $4 + 1$ group of 4
   $= 20 + 4$
   $= 24$
7. 8; 8
8. 36; 36

**Lesson 5**

1. $2 \times 8 = 16$
   So, $16 \div 2 = 8$
   There are 8 bones in each group.
2. $3 \times 7 = 21$
   So, $21 \div 3 = 7$
   There are 7 birds in each group.
3. $5 \times 3 = 15$
   $3 \times 5 = 15$
   $15 \div 3 = 5$
   $15 \div 5 = 3$
4. $5 \times 4 = 20$
   $4 \times 5 = 20$
   $20 \div 4 = 5$
   $20 \div 5 = 4$
5. $4 \times 6 = 24$
   $6 \times 4 = 24$
   $24 \div 4 = 6$
   $24 \div 6 = 4$
6. $10 \times 3 = 30$
   $3 \times 10 = 30$
   $30 \div 3 = 10$
   $30 \div 10 = 3$
7. $6 \times 3 = 18$
   $3 \times 6 = 18$
   $18 \div 3 = 6$
   $18 \div 6 = 3$
8. $9 \times 4 = 36$
   $4 \times 9 = 36$
   $36 \div 4 = 9$
   $36 \div 9 = 4$
9. $24 \div 4 = 6$
   Each boy gets 6 muffins.
10. $27 \div 3 = 9$
    There are 9 plates.
11. $40 \div 4 = 10$
    There are 10 students.

**Put on Your Thinking Cap!**

1. Circle 9, 12, 15, 18, 21, 24, 27, and 30.
   Each sum can be exactly divided by 3.

## Chapter 16

**Lesson 1**

1. $5 \times 4 = 20$
   She puts 20 stamps on envelopes in all.
2. $6 \times 3 = 18$
   There are 18 roses in all.
3. $5 \times 10 = 50$
   She does 50 exercises in 5 days.
4. $10 \times 4 = 40$
   Colleen has 40 pencils in all.
5. $8 \times 3 = 24$
   Alexander has 24 erasers in all.
6. $3 \times 10 = 30$
   The total length of the 3 crayons is 30 centimeters.
7. $6 \times 10 = 60$
   The total length of the 6 ribbons is 60 centimeters.
8. $4 \times 8 = 32$
   Diana has 32 stickers in all.

**Lesson 2**

1. $18 \div 3 = 6$
   She puts 6 roses in each vase.
2. $16 \div 4 = 4$
   There are 4 marbles in each cup.
3. $20 \div 4 = 5$
   There are 5 horses in the stable.
4. $25 \div 5 = 5$
   Mrs. Lewis has 5 children.
5. ?
   45
   $45 \div 5 = 9$
   Each of them gets 9 baseball cards.
6. ?
   15
   $15 \div 3 = 5$
   There are 5 glasses in each row.
7. 28 balloons
   4 4
   ? bunches
   $28 \div 4 = 7$
   The clown has 7 bunches of balloons.

8. ? days

4 | 4

36 pages

$36 \div 4 = 9$

It took Benjie 9 days to read the magazine.

**Lesson 3**

1. Multiply

   $4 \times 8 = 32$

   The lace was 32 centimeters long at first.

2. Divide

   $30 \div 3 = 10$

   Each piece is 10 inches long.

3. Multiply

   3 in.

   ?

   $7 \times 3 = 21$

   The total length of the boxes is 21 inches.

4. Divide

   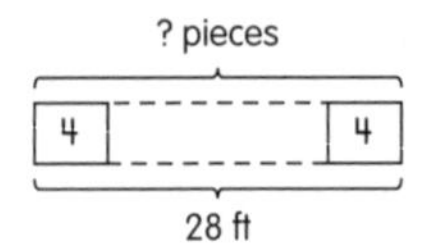
   

   $28 \div 4 = 7$

   She cuts the rope into 7 pieces.

5. Divide

   $30 \div 5 = 6$

   The mass of each bag is 6 kilograms.

6. Divide

   $50 \div 5 = 10$

   There are 10 pens.

7. Multiply

   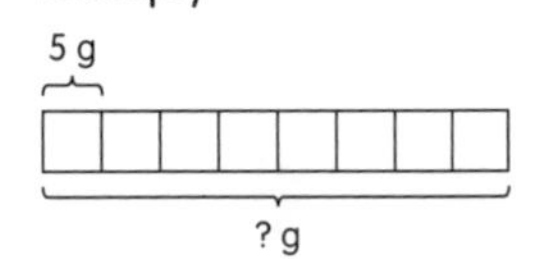
   

   $8 \times 5 = 40$

   The total mass of the 8 crackers is 40 grams.

8. Divide

   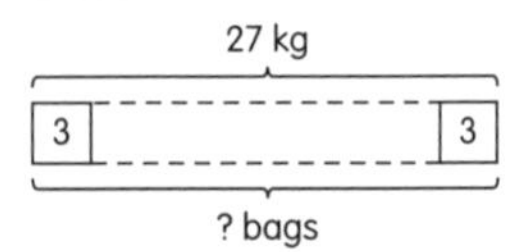
   

   $27 \div 3 = 9$

   There are 9 bags of herbs.

9. Multiply

   $5 \times 5 = 25$

   Mr. Pierson buys 25 liters of juice in 5 weeks.

10. Divide

    $35 \div 5 = 7$

    There are 7 buckets.

11. Multiply

    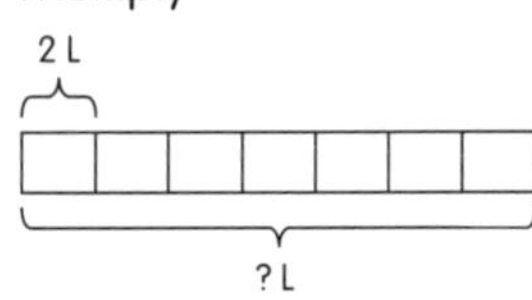
    

    $7 \times 2 = 14$

    Terell drinks 14 liters of water in a week.

12. Divide

    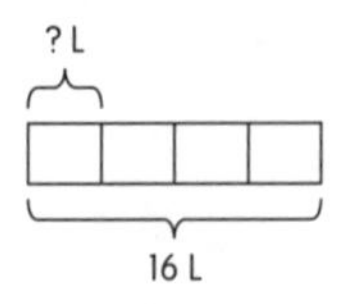
    

    $16 \div 4 = 4$

    There are 4 liters of iced tea in each jug.

13. Multiply

    $4 \times \$5 = \$20$

    Mrs. Talley pays $20 in all.

14. Divide

    $\$32 \div \$8 = 4$

    Mr. Kinnear has 4 children.

15. Multiply

    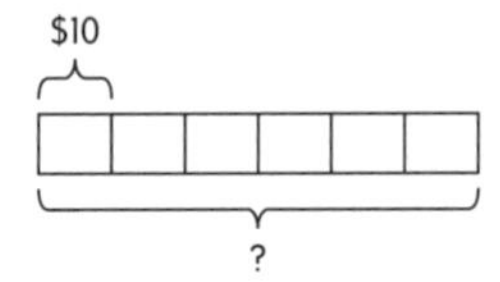
    

    $6 \times \$10 = \$60$

    Pauline gets $60.

16. Divide

    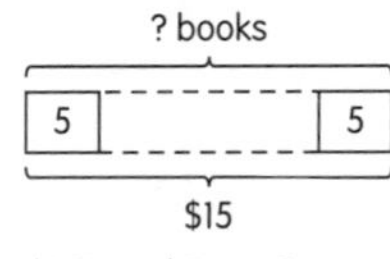
    

    $\$15 \div \$5 = 3$

    Lauren buys 3 books.

**Put on Your Thinking Cap!**

1. 4 baskets of oranges

   3 bags 3 bags

   $2 \times 3 = 6$

   Amy bought 6 bags of oranges.

2. $\$40 \div \$8 = 5$

   She can buy 5 towels.

## Chapter 17

### Lesson 1

1. Each ○ stands for 1 item.
2. Linda bought 4 comic books.
3. She bought the same number of binders as coloring books.
4. She bought 2 more chapter books than crayons.
5. She bought 24 items in all.
6. Two more circles need to be drawn next to 'chapter books'.
7. 6 students like apples.
8. 4 more students like mangoes than pineapples.
9. The most favorite fruit is banana.
10. There are 39 students in the class.
11. Juan has 30 stamps.
12. Ben has the most stamps.
13. Maya has the fewest stamps.
14. Ben has 10 stamps more than Jackson.
15. Maya has 5 stamps fewer than Reza.
16. Maya and Ben have 50 stamps in all.
17. After giving 15 stamps to Jackson, Ben will have 20 stamps left.
18. *Anna Finds A Coin*
19. *The Cup*
20. 20 children have read *The Magic Rose*.
21. 12 more children have read *The Doll* than *The Cup*.
22. The total number of children who have read *The Cup* and *Jilly and The Pear* is 40.

### Lesson 2

1.

| Item | Tally | Number of Items |
|---|---|---|
| Seashells | 卌 卌 \|\| | 12 |
| Pebbles | 卌 \|\|\|\| | 9 |
| Stamps | 卌 卌 卌 卌 \|\|\|\| | 24 |
| Bracelets | 卌 卌 卌 \|\|\| | 18 |
| Marbles | 卌 卌 卌 | 15 |

2.

| Item | Seashells | Pebbles | Stamps | Bracelets | Marbles |
|---|---|---|---|---|---|
| Number of Items | 12 | 9 | 24 | 18 | 15 |

3. **Number of Items**

| Seashells | Pebbles | Stamps | Bracelets | Marbles |
|---|---|---|---|---|
| ▯▯▯▯ | ▯▯▯ | ▯▯▯▯▯▯▯▯ | ▯▯▯▯▯▯ | ▯▯▯▯▯ |

Key: Each ▯ stands for 3 items.

4. There are 18 bracelets.
5. There are 15 marbles.
6.

| Activity | Tally | Number of Children |
|---|---|---|
| Swimming | 卌 卌 \|\| | 12 |
| Jogging | 卌 卌 卌 \| | 16 |
| Tennis | 卌 \|\|\| | 8 |
| Badminton | 卌 卌 \|\| | 12 |
| Squash | 卌 卌 卌 \|\|\| | 18 |

7. **Activities the Children Do**

| Activity | |
|---|---|
| Swimming | ○○○○○○ |
| Jogging | ○○○○○○○○ |
| Tennis | ○○○○ |
| Badminton | ○○○○○○ |
| Squash | ○○○○○○○○○ |

Each ○ stands for 2 children.

8. 66 children go to the sports complex in all.

### Lesson 3

1. 9
2. 3
3. 12
4. **Title: Stones of Different Colors**

| Red | Blue | Yellow | Green | Purple |
|---|---|---|---|---|
| △△△ | △△△△△ | △△△△△△△△ | △△△△△△△ | △△△△△ |

Key: Each △ stands for 3 stones.

## Lesson 4

1.

| Name | Number of Letters | Name | Number of Letters |
|---|---|---|---|
| Jessica | 7 | Barry | 5 |
| Brenda | 6 | Zoe | 3 |
| Carl | 4 | Ann | 3 |
| Fiona | 5 | Nicole | 6 |

2.

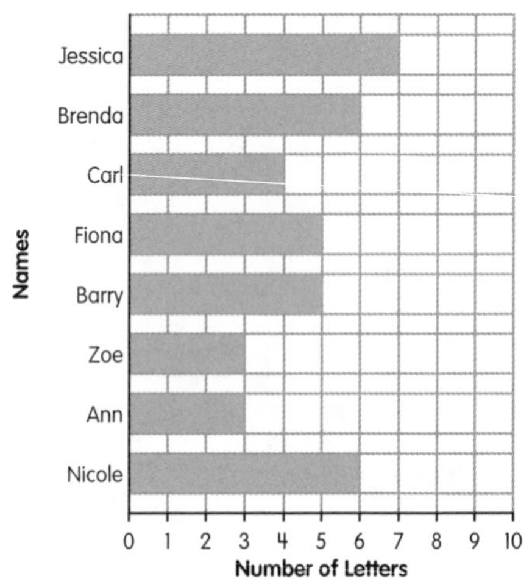


3.

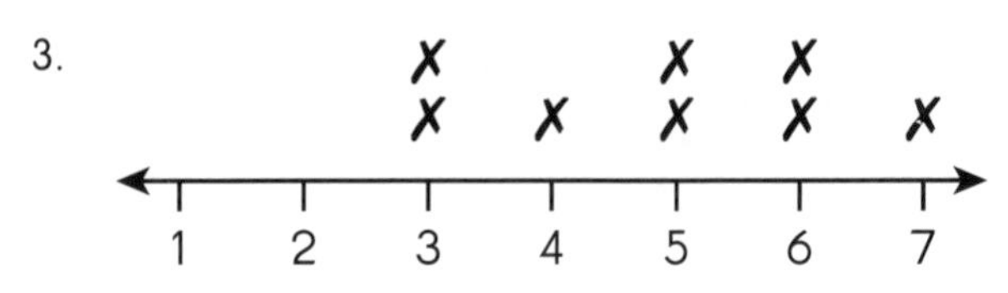


4. 15
5. 24
6. 4
7. 2
8.

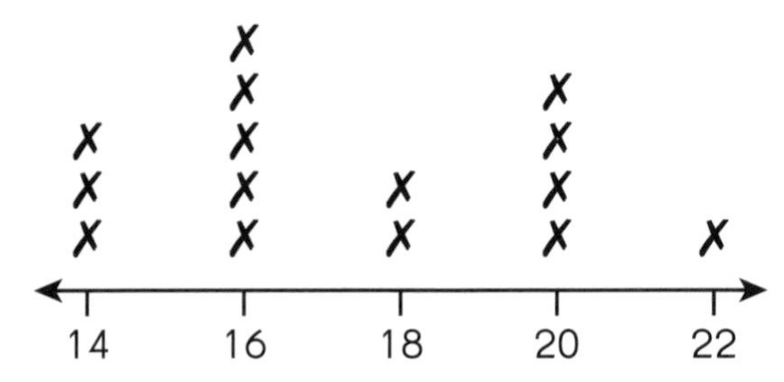


9. 15
10. 16
11. 14
12. 5
13. 13
14. 2
15. 2
16. 3

**Put on Your Thinking Cap!**

Thinking skill: Deduction

Strategy: Use guess and check

Solution:

1. **Items in Different Albums**

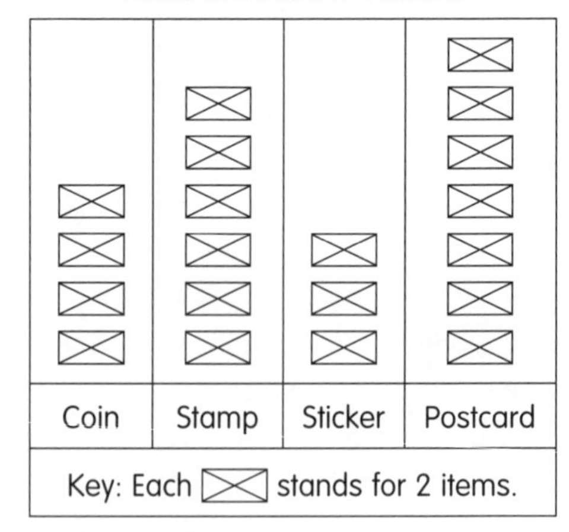


2. Album 1 contains coins.
3. Album 4 contains stamps.
4. Album 2 contains stickers.
5. Album 3 contains postcards.

## Chapter 18

### Lesson 1

1. The figure has 3 parts of lines and 2 curves.
2. The figure has 2 parts of lines and 6 curves.
3. The figure has 6 parts of lines and 5 (accept 1) curves.
4. 4
5. 8 and 3
6. 5, b, and e
7. Answers vary.
   Sample answer: h
8.
9. 8, 8
10. 8, 4
11. 10, 5
12. Answers vary.
    Sample answer:

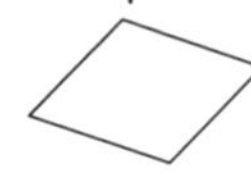

13. Answers vary.
Sample answer:

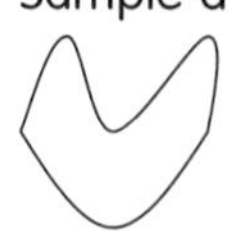

14. Answers vary.
Sample answer:

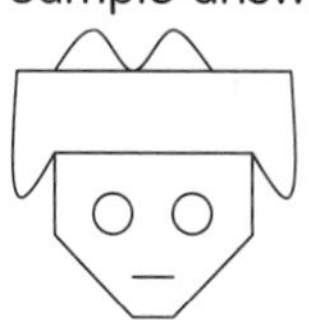

**Lesson 2**

| Object | Number of flat surfaces | Number of curved surfaces |
|---|---|---|
| A | 6 | 0 |
| B | 2 | 1 |
| C | 1 | 1 |
| D | 6 | 0 |
| E | Accept 4 or 5 | 0 |
| F | 5 | 0 |

2. 2, 1
3. 1
4. 6
5. Circle the cylinder and the cube.
6. Circle the sphere and the cone.
7. Circle the pyramid, cube, and cone.

**Put on Your Thinking Cap!**

1. Thinking skill: Spatial visualization
Strategy: Use a diagram
Solution:

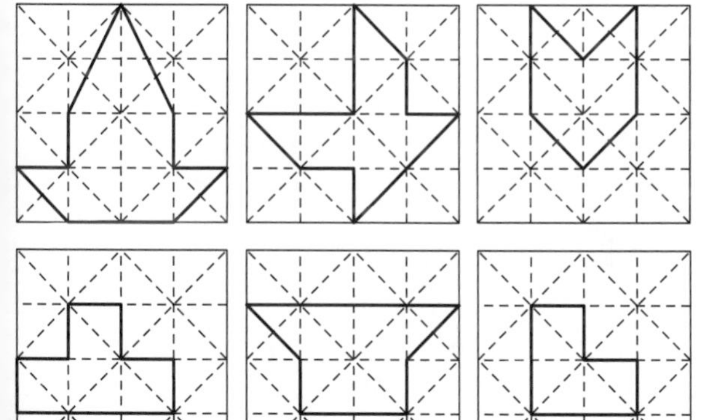

## Chapter 19

**Lesson 1**

1. Color the hexagons red, the circles blue, the triangles yellow, the rectangles green, and the trapezoids purple.
2. Answers vary.
Sample answer:

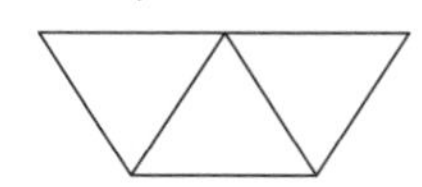

3. Answers vary.
Sample answer:

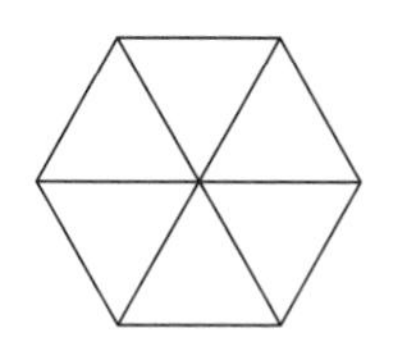

4. Answers vary.
Sample answer:

5. Answers vary.
Sample answers:

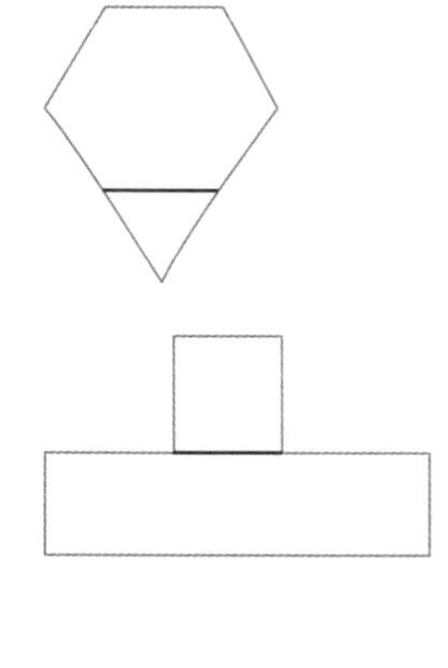

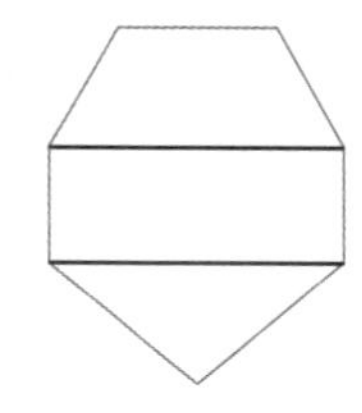

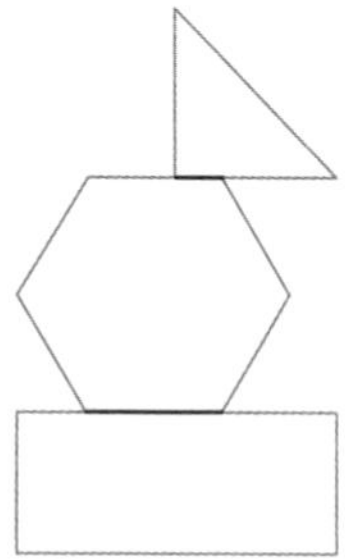

6. rectangle, triangle
7. hexagon, rectangle
8. square, circle
9. trapezoid, square
10.
11.

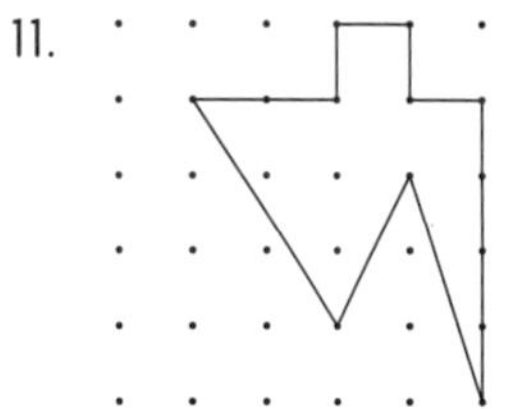

12. 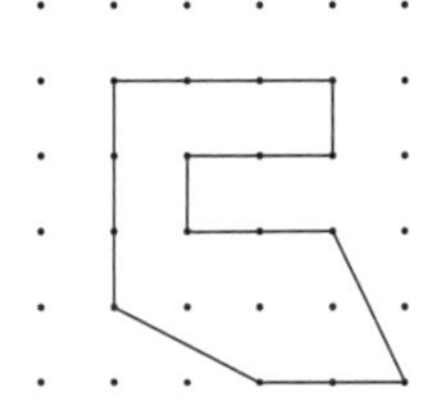

13. 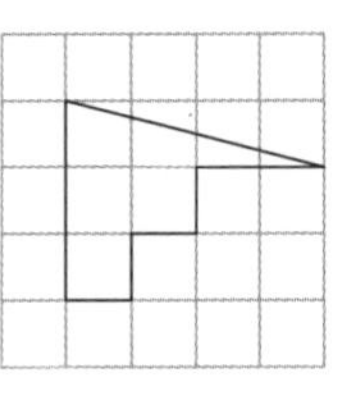

14. 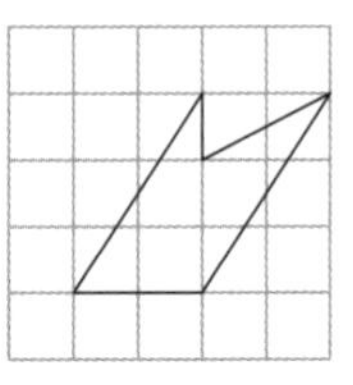

15. 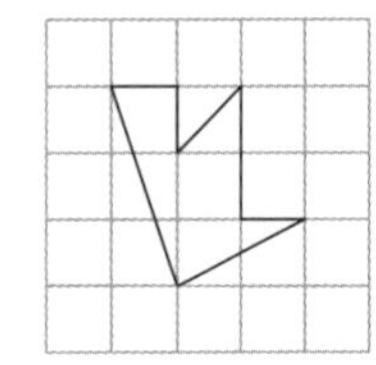

16. 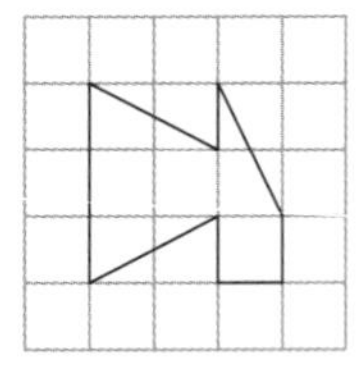

17. 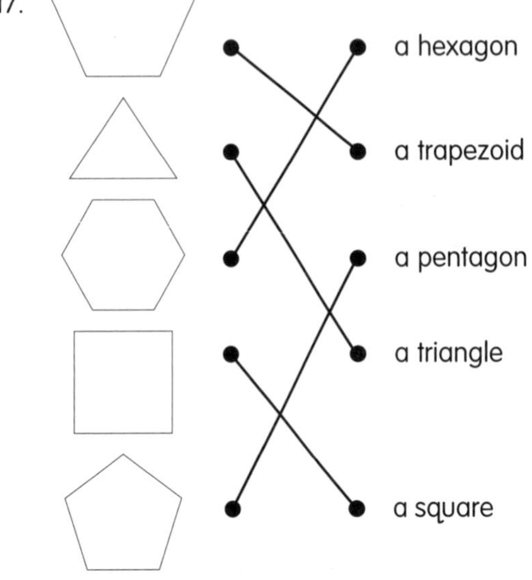


18. I am a triangle.
19. I am a quadrilateral.
20. I am a square.
21. I am a pentagon.
22. I am a hexagon.
23. I am a rectangle.

**Lesson 2**

1.

| Object | Number |
|---|---|
| | 5 |
| | 0 |
| | 1 |
| | 1 |

2.

| Object | Number |
|---|---|
| | 4 |
| | 4 |
| | 2 |
| | 2 |

3.

| Solid Shape | Number |
|---|---|
| Rectangular prism | 1 (or 4) |
| Cube | 3 |
| Cone | 2 |
| Cylinder | 3 |
| Sphere | 2 |

4. Draw lines on the cube to show how it is made of six faces.

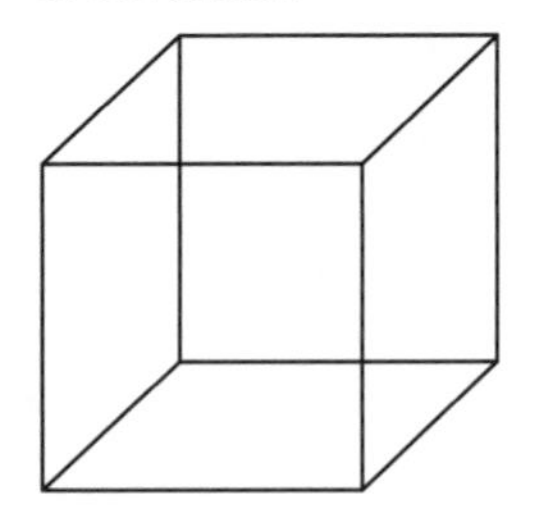

**Lesson 3**

1.

2. 

3. 

4. Circle 

5. Circle 

**Put on Your Thinking Cap!**

1. Thinking skill: Spatial visualization
   Strategy: Act it out
   Solution: Group A

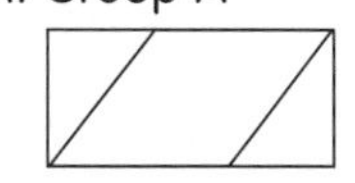

2. Thinking skill: Classifying
   Strategy: Act it out

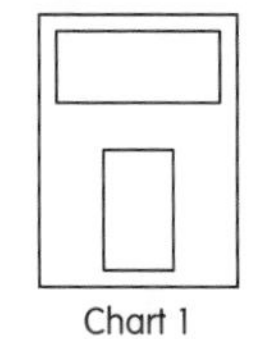
Chart 1

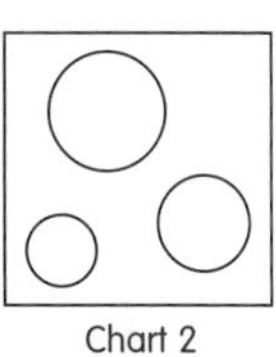
Chart 2

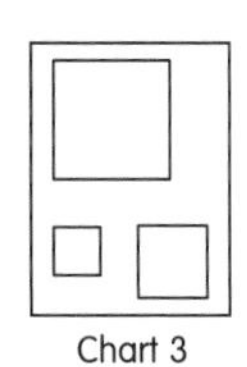
Chart 3

Chart 4

## End-of-year Test Prep

| | | | | | | | |
|---|---|---|---|---|---|---|---|
| 1. | D | 2. | C | 3. | B | 4. | C |
| 5. | C | 6. | B | 7. | A | 8. | D |
| 9. | C | 10. | C | 11. | C | 12. | D |
| 13. | A | 14. | C | 15. | A | 16. | C |
| 17. | D | 18. | B | 19. | B | 20. | A |

21. 526
22. $27 + 43 = 70$
    There are 70 bows in all.
23.

24. She takes the cake out of the oven at 3:30.
25.

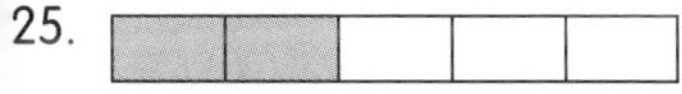

26. \$0.95
27. Circle \$35.00
28. $58 - 46 = 12$
    Sam collects 12 more seashells on Tuesday than on Monday.
29.

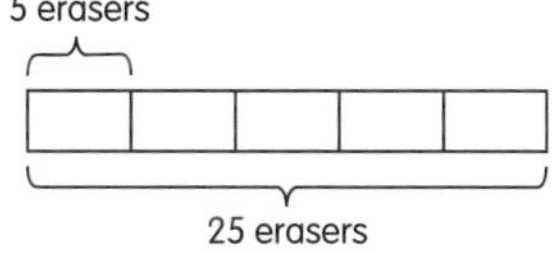


$25 \div 5 = 5$
Each friend gets 5 erasers.

30. a. The pair of glasses is 5 inches long.
    b. The candle is 4 inches longer than the pair of glasses.
31. The picture is made with 10 parts of lines and 5 curves.
32. \$5

    ?

    $4 \times \$5 = \$20$
    They receive \$20 in all.
33.
34. He reaches his friend's house at 7:30.
35. ☺
36. He will get a circle.
37. 12
38. She buys a book and a pen.
39. $\$25 + \$25 + \$23 = \$73$
    $\$73 - \$45 = \$28$
    He needs \$28 more.
40. Accept 4 or 5.
41. 682 stamps 239 stamps

    921 stamps

    $682 + 239 = 921$
    He has 921 stamps in all.
42.

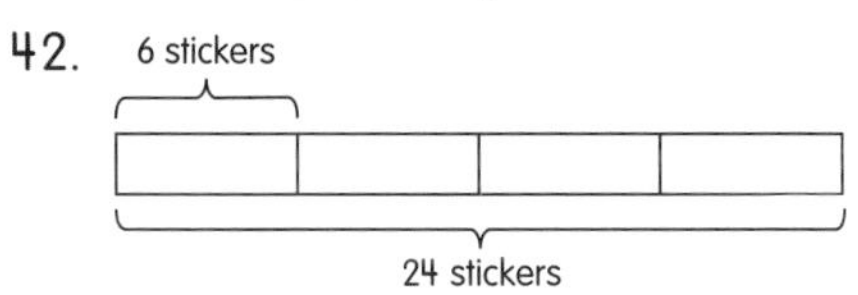


$24 \div 4 = 6$
He puts 6 stickers on each chart.

43.

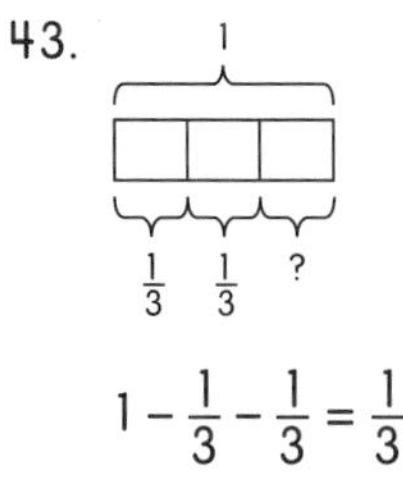


$1 - \frac{1}{3} - \frac{1}{3} = \frac{1}{3}$

$\frac{1}{3}$ of the muffin is left.

44.

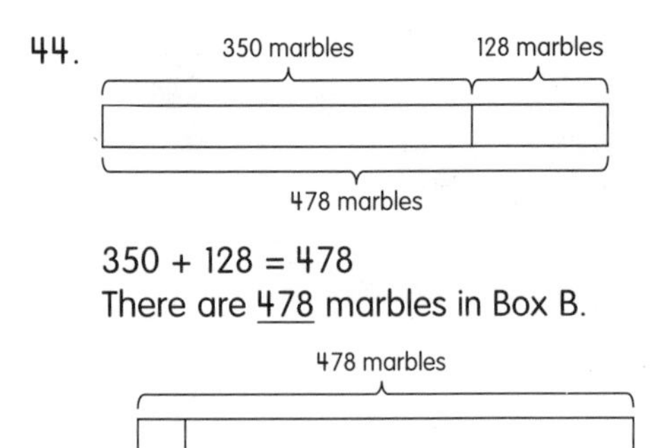


350 + 128 = 478

There are 478 marbles in Box B.

478 marbles

45 marbles ? marbles

478 – 45 = 433

There are 433 marbles in Box C.

45. a.

| Number of goals | 0 | 1 | 2 | 3 | 4 | 5 |
|---|---|---|---|---|---|---|
| Number of players | 5 | 9 | 6 | 3 | 5 | 2 |

b. 30

c. 1

d. 2